HUNTING POWDER

A SKIER'S GUIDE TO FINDING COLORADO'S BEST SNOW

BY
JORDAN LIPP

Foreword by Joel Gratz

ISBN: 978-0-578-83853-3 (paperback)
Cover Design by Zoe Kaatz
www.zoekaatz.com

Table of Contents

Disclaimer

Skiing and its related sports like snowboarding, telemark skiing, etc. are inherently dangerous. Needless to say, hunting powder, hunting groomers, hunting corn, hunting sand, and all other activities discussed in this book are inherently dangerous. (Okay, reading the computer model forecasts on your laptop at your house isn't dangerous, but everything else discussed in this book is.) Dangers include, among many others, falls, collisions, avalanches, snow immersion suffocations, snow conditions, weather, and exposure. This book is not a substitute for education, experience, knowledge, and sound judgment. The author and all those involved in the writing, publication, and sale of this book assume no liability for the information contained within this book or for any problems that may arise from this book in any manner.

Foreword

Colorado does not receive the most snow, nor is it the place with the steepest terrain, and it is not the region with the most ski areas. If that's the case, then why do so many people ski and ride in the Centennial State? The answer is that the draw to Colorado lies not in a single factor but the combination of all factors. Plentiful snow, diverse terrain, lots of inbounds and backcountry areas, and numerous mountain towns all add up to a place where people come for one winter and wind up spending a lifetime.

While skiing and riding brings joy in many forms, from cruising fresh groomers to hop-turning down 50-degree couloirs, for many people, the most memorable days of the season are the ones that offer the deepest and fluffiest powder.

But powder is tricky. It is perishable, which increases its allure and also the difficulty in finding it. And powder in big mountains turns out to be difficult to forecast since these mountains can create weather patterns that are not perfectly modeled by today's sophisticated forecasting systems.

I learned the trickiness of forecasting powder shortly after I moved to Colorado. With a meteorology degree and an obsession for skiing, I should have never missed a storm. Yet I did miss out on many storms, including a 48-inch snowfall in 48-hours at Steamboat (yes, 15 years later, I am still mad that I missed this one). After missing that four-footer at Steamboat, I swore that I would figure out mountain weather patterns in Colorado and try my best to not miss the next deep powder day.

So I spent my nights and weekends researching and learning winter weather patterns in Colorado, and this included figuring out what storm tracks and wind directions produce more snow than most forecasts show. Eventually, when my confidence became just a bit higher than my fear of failure, I started a friends and family email list that focused on answering the question, "When and where will we find the best powder?"

That 37-person email list is now a website and an app called OpenSnow, which is a service that delivers powder forecasts to over 2 million people and has forecasters like me across the United States and Canada. I created OpenSnow to help people find great powder without needing to open 20 browser tabs to check multiple forecasts and ski area websites. I also created OpenSnow so that my meteorology degree and years of powder-forecasting research could mean that people would not need to have their own meteorology degree to figure out where and when to find the best powder.

After a decade of writing about winter weather patterns in Colorado, making the science of meteorology relatable, and tying the science together with the goal of chasing the deepest powder, a funny thing happened. I started to get emails from people that wanted more geeky weather details. These folks often said that if they didn't pursue their current career of an engineer, a teacher, an accountant, a lawyer, or a ski bum, they really would have wanted to be a meteorologist, or at least learn a lot more about the weather.

And that's the exact person that will love this book– someone who obsesses over powder in Colorado and wants to learn more about meteorology but doesn't want to go back to school for a degree in Atmospheric Science.

The author of this book, Jordan Lipp, is an experienced skier, having written the guidebook about Berthoud Pass and having skied over 100 areas in the US and on most of the continents in the world. Jordan loves powder, skiing, and terrain, and obsesses over it, but he's actually a lawyer and not a meteorologist. If that's the case, then is this book legit? Actually, I think it is, and I think that Jordan's lack of a meteorology degree is a feature rather than a bug.

Jordan taught himself meteorology and then worked hard to translate dense textbooks into concepts that powder-obsessed skiers could understand. A meteorology professor might quibble with a few of the ways that Jordan presents the information. But you are not concerned with acing an end-of-semester meteorology exam and rather want to know more details about why the atmosphere gives the gift of deep, blower powder. And that's what this book is all about. So dig in, feel free to skip around if the science becomes too dense in spots, and remember that the goal of this book is to help you to miss fewer powder days. And who knows, maybe I'll see you in the trees the next time the atmosphere smiles on Steamboat with a couple feet of fluff.

Joel Gratz
Founding Meteorologist & CEO
OpenSnow
https://opensnow.com

Acknowledgments

This book would not be possible without the extraordinary contributions of numerous people. I was fortunate enough to have expert input on various portions of the manuscript from five different brilliant individuals.

First, Joel Gratz, my favorite Colorado meteorologist and snow forecaster, provided numerous comments and suggestions. I cannot thank him enough for his insights and suggested changes.

Second, Professor Brian Rosser was instrumental in advice and guidance on the various operations portions of this book. I am fortunate to have received his insights, and I envy his students who can learn from him every day.

Third, my mentor, the avalanche guru Lin Ballard, provided fantastic feedback on the chapters on recycled powder and avalanches.

Fourth, Paul Baugher, the leading authority in the United States on snow immersion suffocation, was kind enough to provide extensive thoughts on the snow immersion suffocation chapter.

Fifth, my fellow ski patroller Ben Hogan, who did his master's degree in upper atmospheric modeling, provided invaluable advice on explaining fluid dynamics and computer modeling in this book.

I was similarly fortunate enough to have family and friends review various iterations of the manuscript – providing me guidance on readability and approach. They are my wife Heather, my parents Dan and Ronnie, and my fellow ski patroller Ken Dykes. Ken was also kind enough to contribute some of his photographs for the book.

Also, although they were not involved in the writing or editing of this book, I have learned so much from reading the thoughts of and/or listening to the lectures of some of the great weather forecasters and atmospheric scientists in Colorado, including, to name a few, Sam Collentine, Lisa Kriederman, Seth Linden, John Snook, and Klaus Wolter. Their forecasts and lectures (as well as, of course, Joel Gratz's amazing forecasts and lectures), have been so important in my development and learning.

I cannot thank enough all of my fellow ski patrollers on the Bryan Mountain Nordic Ski Patrol, who have helped with and encouraged both my ski patrol weather forecasts and my teaching of the topics in this book in our ski patrol avalanche and mountaineering classes.

My children were amazingly patient with me, as children are, as the book endlessly crept into our lives as I slowly wrote and revised the book. For example, my poor kids had to hear about adiabatic cooling every time we deflated a paddleboard and felt the cool air rush out of the deflating board.

Finally, I owe the most to my wife Heather for putting up with me as I researched and wrote this book over the last five and a half years.

Please bear in mind that despite the invaluable assistance described above, the ultimate decision of what suggested edits to include or not include were made solely by me. Any and all errors in this book (and there are bound to be many errors in any book of this scope and type) are, of course, all mine.

Introduction

Colorado is, without fear of exaggeration, world-famous for its skiing. And rightfully so. With some of the most legendary ski resorts in the world – Aspen, Breckenridge, Steamboat, Telluride, and Vail, to name only a few – and with its famed dry powder, few places on Earth can compare to the volume and quality of Colorado skiing. It has all the ingredients for exceptional skiing. Colorado is roughly a thousand miles from the nearest ocean, resulting in its legendary snow quality. Colorado has both copious amounts of snowfall and copious amounts of sunshine in which to enjoy the fresh powder. It is of no surprise that when measured by skier-visit days, Colorado is far and away the most popular state for skiing in the United States.

But snow is the result of weather, and as every person knows, weather can be unpredictable. Whether you live in the Centennial State and ski every day, or you are planning a once in a lifetime ski trip to Colorado, the quality of the skiing on any given day will be dependent upon the snow and weather. My goal is to provide you, the reader, with the best ideas about when and where to ski in our great state and how to find and ski as much powder as possible. To help you optimize knowing where and when to ski, I've spent countless hours researching and writing this book, as well as countless absolutely essential hours skiing and snowboarding Colorado's mountains in all conditions over all twelve months of the year for many years. (It's a rough life.)

While there is lots of powder in the Colorado Mountains, it is no easy task to predict when and where you'll find the most and best of it. As the old joke goes: *meteorology makes astrology seem like a hard science.* But this is only a joke – everyone knows that reliance on a weather forecast is far more predictable than reliance on a horoscope – even if forecasts are frustratingly wrong more often than we'd like them to be. Slowly but surely, forecasting snowfall is improving. And, there are always better places than others to find good powder. Indeed, there are predictable long-term patterns in snow fall.

The more you know about meteorology and climatology, the easier it is to hunt for powder. That is the aim of this book. I hope to provide an easy to read and entertaining look at mountain meteorology, Colorado's climatology, and related tips on finding the best powder skiing.

That said, while there are no equations in this book, I nevertheless do not shy away from difficult concepts and on occasion, rather long words. After all, your ability to hunt for great snow depends on having a fundamental understanding of the science and the ability to interpret forecast discussions. In spite of some long words, however, I'll keep the tone light and fun. We are, after all, talking about skiing.

First, a note about the word "skiing." This book is written for all sports that enjoy riding powder – whether downhill skiing, snowboarding, telemarking, AT skiing, etc. However, as it takes too long to mention each sport in turn, to save space I just write about skiers and skiing. No offense snowboarders – I love to snowboard as well as ski. I'm just using the simplest language.

How is this book organized? The first part of this book is an introduction to basic meteorology and the five methods by which snow is produced in Colorado. The second part of this book is a quick look at the micro scale of snow, the macro scale of weather, and combining all the concepts of the first two parts of the book into a discussion of one of the great blizzards of this century so far. With these meteorological concepts out of the way, the third part of the book discusses weather models, which constitute the backbone of every weather forecast. In the fourth part, I turn the three previous parts into the lessons of both home weather forecasting and following the professional forecasters.

The first four parts of the book only get to the point when the snow has fallen, but you're not skiing falling snow. Rather, in order to hunt powder once the snow is on the ground, it's important to understand how wind and temperature affect the snow that has fallen, which is the focus of the fifth part of the book. The sixth part of the book discusses Colorado's snow climate regions and provides additional tips on hunting powder based upon forecasts and how best to find powder once you are skiing at a ski resort. The seventh part of the book discusses some of the myriad of dangers involved with powder hunting. Understanding the dangers helps skiers change their actions in order to reduce (though one often cannot eliminate) the risk from those dangers. And, although this book is about powder, I would be remiss if I did not discuss a few of the non-powder joys of skiing, and how to find them in Colorado, whether finding the best corn snow or the best sand skiing. So, those subjects constitute the eighth and final portion of this book. And, if you still haven't had enough, I have many appendices to provide further information on all sorts of the topics discussed in the book.

Although there may be an illusion of order and logic in the flow of the book, for what it's worth, the chapters in this book are written to be read in any order as you see fit. Read whichever chapters interest you, and the chapters will cross-reference each other when you need to know content from one chapter for another chapter. This naturally leads to a little repetitiveness at some points, but I strive to at least describe the same concepts from different angles and emphases each time. And a little variable repetitiveness can help drive home concepts.

If you want to start with how weather models work and what are the major weather models, you can begin with Chapters 10 and 11. If you want to start with my powder day pointers of maximizing your powder at a ski area, start with Chapter 26. If you want a primer on corn snow, you can begin with Chapter 33. Don't feel as if you need to plod through every scientific detail in the book – every reader will take away different amounts of information from this book. And, for better or worse, the densest reading overall is in the earlier portions of this book, and slowly but surely the science and concepts tend to get easier in the later portions of the book.

In the following pages, I hope to provide you with as much information as possible, so that you can make the best decisions on when and where to have the highest odds of unbelievably great Colorado powder days.

Happy powder hunting, and let's jump in.

PART 1

WHY DOES IT SNOW (OR NOT SNOW)

Why does it snow? It's tough to hunt powder without at least a basic under-standing of the answer to this critical question. Let's tackle this question by first reviewing the three basic principles that cause snow, which is the subject of the first and brief chapter. In short, snow is produced by moist air being lifted in elevation.

Each of the following chapters will explore the various ways that moist air is lifted in elevation, which causes snow. Hint, the biggest cause of lift are mountains, so I'll devote two chapters to this critical concept. Then, I'll devote a chapter each to the next two biggest causes of snow (low pressure and jet streaks). And, I'll relegate the less impactful causes of snow into the final chapter of this part of the book.

Let's start with the basics.

Chapter 1

Weather 101: The Three Principles Behind Snowfall

For those who have a basic understanding of meteorology, feel free to skip this chapter, and just start with Chapter 2. But for those who are either new to the concepts of meteorology, or just want a refresher, read on. In order to understand where and when it snows, it's critical to understand three fundamental principles. And, it won't take long to explain them.

Principle One: It Gets Colder the Higher You Go in the Atmosphere. Most people who spend time in the mountains are quite familiar with the concept that it's usually colder the higher one gets in elevation. I never take warm clothes for the bottom of hiking a 14er. No one ever talks about snowcapped valleys. And its typically coldest getting off the highest lift at the ski area as opposed to loading onto the chairlift at the bottom of the mountain.

The amount of decrease in temperature as one goes higher in elevation varies hour by hour and day by day – and on occasion even reverses. That said, as a very rough rule of thumb, figure the temperature decreases by 4 degrees Fahrenheit for every 1000' in elevation gain. So, for example, my house in Golden sits on the side of Lookout Mountain at 6,000'. The top of Lookout Mountain, a little over 1,200' above my house, averages roughly 5 degrees colder than my house. Downtown Golden, roughly 250' below my house, is just slightly warmer, roughly 1 degree warmer, than my house. This is why occasionally I'll see snow only on the upper half of Lookout Mountain.

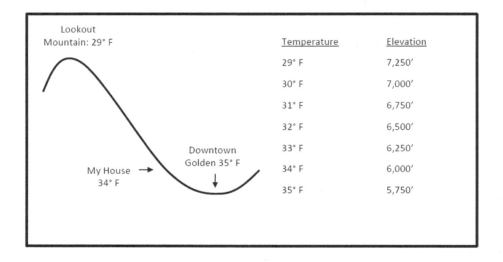

Lookout
Mountain: 29° F

Temperature	Elevation
29° F	7,250'
30° F	7,000'
31° F	6,750'
32° F	6,500'
33° F	6,250'
34° F	6,000'
35° F	5,750'

Downtown
Golden 35° F

My House →
34° F

Principle Two: Cold Air Cannot Hold as Much Moisture as Warm Air. Unlike the first principle, that as one goes higher it gets colder, the second principle is a little less obvious. But it is absolutely critical to understand why it snows. Cold air cannot hold as much moisture in it as warm air.[1]

Although this may not sound obvious at first blush, you know this intuitively. Let me explain. Your house or apartment in the winter feels much drier than it does in the summer – even if you keep it the same temperature all year round. The reason why is that the house pulls in the outside air. In the winter, that outside air cannot hold much moisture. The humidity may be 90 percent on a cold snowy day outside, but as your house's heater heats this 90% humid air to a comfortable living temperature inside, all of a sudden that moist outside air feels dry inside your house? Why? Because warm air can hold much more moisture, so the humidity (which is a percent of the total moisture air can hold) drops drastically when the moist air from outside is brought into your house and heated. This is even more apparent when

---

[1]   From a technical standpoint it would probably be more proper to say that cold air reaches saturation and creates precipitation with less moisture than does warm air, but saying that cold air cannot hold as much moisture as warm air is good enough for our purposes.

you blast the heater in your car after it's been sitting outside all day as you ski during a snowstorm. The outside air feels wet, but when it's heated in your car the percentage of moisture drops drastically making it feel dry.

Indeed, as crazy as it sounds, there's more total moisture in the air in the dry summer heat of Colorado than during a cold snowstorm in the middle of winter. I know this is not quite as obvious as principle one, but it's key in understanding why snow occurs.

Principle Three: Moist Air That is Lifted Higher in Elevation is What Creates Snow. Putting together principles one and two, when moist air is raised in elevation, it gets colder. And as cold air cannot hold as much moisture as warm air, the excess moisture must go somewhere. The cold air lets go of that excess moisture in the form of snow. As moist air rises, it cools and therefore it snows.

One of my favorite ways to illustrate this concept is based upon a night of drinking in the mountains. (Trust me, as this is a book for skiers, there will be lots of drinking examples throughout the book.) Years ago, my wife and I were car camping with our kids near Leadville, Colorado in July. On a clear beautiful night, after the kids went to sleep, we fixed ourselves Black Russians (Vodka, Kahlua, and ice) in plastic cups. Shortly after making our drinks late on the beautiful summer night, seemingly by magic, ice formed in a ring on the outside of our plastic cups. These rings of ice around the outside of the cup were at the same height as the ice cubes inside the cup. As we drank our drinks, the magically appearing ice rings slowly moved down the outside of the plastic cups, always staying at the same height as the ice inside the cup. What was going on? Hint: it wasn't magic. Rather, the air always has moisture in it. That's true even on a beautiful summer night in the mountains. The ice inside our cups had cooled down the air just outside of the cups enough for the moisture in the air to freeze all around the outside of the cup. Our ice cubes were basically mimicking what would happen if the air around us was raised in elevation to the point that it was nearly as cold the nearby ice cubes. Cooling the temperature of air, whether through ice in alcoholic drinks or lifting the air to a higher elevation, turns the water vapor into ice crystals.

Everyone with me so far? The key concept is that it snows when moist air is lifted in elevation enough so the moist air cools enough that it must let go of the excess moisture in the form of snow. (If this is still a bit unclear, don't worry. I'll revisit this concept with various examples in the next several chapters as we start to dive into what causes air to lift.)

As the key to snowfall is moist air lifting, by far the most important question in meteorology to skiers is what causes moist air to rise in elevation. The next five chapters are devoted to this question. Let's start with the most important method that causes moist air to lift – mountains.

Chapter 2

Imagine You Are a Cloud: How Mountains Create Snow

Let's start with a thought experiment. Imagine that you are a cloud. Let's track how you are born, your journey to Colorado, and how and where as you pass through Colorado you produce extraordinary powder for the skiers. This mental exercise, as juvenile as it may sound, will introduce many of the key concepts of meteorology to know where, when, and why we get great powder.

So, visualize yourself as a cloud. Okay, technically, you are not a cloud, but rather you are an air parcel with at least a decent amount of water vapor in it. However, it's hard to visualize yourself as a parcel of air because you cannot see air. And, the title of the chapter is far catchier as: "imagine you are a cloud," than "imagine you are an air parcel with water vapor." So, we'll stick with the term "cloud," although it's just slightly inaccurate.[2]

---

[2] If you really care why saying you are a cloud is technically inaccurate for this thought experiment – though still close enough to the truth to understand the fundamentals of snow – here is a quick description of the difference between a parcel of air with water vapor in it and a cloud.

Water vapor is always in the air (that's what we call humidity). There's never no humidity – and humidity levels even in the desert are still usually in the double digits. Once the water vapor contained in the air falls below a certain temperature, the water vapor condenses on tiny particles floating in the air (think, for example, specks of dust) to form droplets. When there is a sufficient mass of droplets, these droplets become visible as clouds floating in

Where you the cloud are born

Snoqualmie Pass, WA, elev. 3,021'

Parley's Summit, UT, elev. 7,120'

Vail Pass, CO, elev. 10,662'
Loveland Pass, CO, elev. 11,991'

the sky. What is a sufficient mass? Well let's put it this way. Millions of water droplets would fit into the size of the period at the end of this sentence.

You know how on a really cold day you can see your own breath? That's because your breath is more humid than the surrounding air, and once it enters the cold air, it condenses (just like water vapor forming a cloud). But this only works if it's cold. On a warm day this does not happen – you cannot see your own breath. So water vapor is only visible (i.e., condenses to become a cloud) when there is both (1) enough water vapor in the air and (2) the air gets cold enough. Take away either piece (either your humid breath or the cold air) and there is no cloud.

Your trip that will be described in this chapter will have times you are visible as a cloud. And it will have other times that you are not visible. Regardless, you will remain the same air parcel throughout the journey.

YOUR BIRTH (THE PACIFIC OCEAN)

You will be born, so to speak, over the greatest moisture producer in the world, none other than the Pacific Ocean. The ocean, after all, is filled with water. And, as water evaporates into the atmosphere, it will form you the cloud.

You'll likely be born near the Aleutian Islands, a bit south of Alaska, though you could be born as far south as Hawaii. And as you were born over the ocean, as opposed to over land, you will have lots of moisture in you.

What happens next? You will be blown towards North America. How do we know that? Because, although there are always exceptions, as a general rule of thumb winds blow from west to east in our part of the world. That is one of the reasons why surfing in California is awesome, and surfing in Florida is lame. (Sorry Florida, but it's true.) That is why flying from New York to Denver takes longer than flying from Denver to New York. And, that is why the base of Steamboat Ski Resort sees more snow than Evergreen, even though Evergreen is at a higher elevation. But, I'm getting ahead of myself.

The westerly winds will carry you from your birthplace over the Pacific Ocean to the North American continent. You may first hit land in Alaska, Mexico, or somewhere in between. And now, your land journey to Colorado will begin. (Let's hope the winds bring you to Colorado, because a slightly different direction could bring you to Montana instead, and then the lucky skiers at Big Sky as opposed to Aspen will be enjoying your snow.)

YOUR FIRST SNOWFALL (WASHINGTON)

After you hit land, when you get close to your first mountain, the magic will begin. Let's take what we learned in Chapter 1, and expand our understanding. Although the term is a mouthful, the term for this magic is important, and in my mind forms the greatest two words in the English Language — *orographic lifting*.

Orographic lifting is the reason why there is snow on the mountains. It is the reason why you can ski powder. It is the source of the mighty Arkansas, Colorado, and Rio Grande Rivers (all of which originate in Colorado). It is the reason why you can go white-water rafting and fly-fishing in Colorado, and it is the reason why there is enough water (if barely) to supply the towns, ski areas, and farms of Colorado with sufficient water. Indeed, without orographic lifting, the powder skiing in Nebraska would be as good as the powder skiing in Colorado. So, is it really an overstatement to claim that "orographic lifting" is the greatest two-word combination in the English language?

So, what is orographic lifting? Here's how I explain it to my little kids – which is a close enough description to be able to understand when and where it snows, even if it's not terribly scientific. I tell my kids: "As the winds push the clouds over the tall mountains where it's cold, the clouds get cold and shiver until the shivering produces snow."

Okay, technically the clouds don't shiver as they rise. But it's somewhat close. As the winds push clouds to a higher elevation to get over the mountains, the clouds go through *adiabatic cooling*. Adiabatic cooling is just the fancy scientific term that (for our intents and purposes) means that it gets colder as you get higher in elevation. When you deflate your paddleboard or your bicycle tires, if you place your hand over the escaping air, you'll notice that it's cold. That is adiabatic cooling – under more pressure air is warmer and under less pressure it is cooler.

You don't need to understand the details of adiabatic cooling to understand that the result of clouds being pushed to a higher elevation to go over a mountain is that they cool, which leads to snow (or, in the summer, rain). Just remember, as discussed in Chapter 1, it's generally colder the higher you go in the mountains. So, the cloud cools as it climbs up and over a mountain. Cooling clouds create snow.

This is the key. Winds push clouds up the side of a mountain until their temperature cools enough to cause snow (i.e., the temperature in the clouds lowers to the dew point temperature and beyond, which means the cloud becomes super-saturated, and the condensation, pulled downward by gravity, produces precipitation).

So, the ingredients of snow are (i) moisture in the air, (ii) winds, and (iii) mountains. As long as the winds are blowing the moist air up the mountains, there's snow. It's that simple.

Back to you as a cloud. Let's say you strike land somewhere near Seattle, Washington. As you rise up over the Olympic and Cascade Mountains of Washington, you make sure to cool down enough to lightly rain over Seattle. But as you're climbing Steven's Pass (4,055') or Snoqualmie Pass (3,021'), you've cooled enough so the rain you are producing turns to snow. Not the light precipitation over Seattle either. With a belly full of that moisture from the Pacific Ocean and a rise in elevation, you snow like mad. It is little wonder that the snow you produce at this point – having just hit land after leaving the Pacific Ocean – will be deep. And, as the ocean is warmer than the land in winter (as discussed more in Chapter 7), you will not only produce lots of snow, but the snow will tend to be heavy and wet. This is why Mount Baker Ski Area in Washington holds the record for annual snowfall – 95 feet of snow – for the winter of 1998-1999.

Although often referred to derogatorily as Sierra Cement, Seattle Cement, or Cascade Concrete, the technical name for this heavy wet snow is *maritime* snow.[3] And, considering that maritime snow holds on steeper faces than our snow in Colorado, and tends to last later into the summer, we shouldn't poo-poo this type of snow too much.

Once again, back to you as a cloud. You just dumped a lot of heavy wet snow in the Cascade Mountains of Washington State, and your journey to Colorado will now continue. Just as you had to rise over the mountains and produce precipitation, now that the winds are blowing you down the backside of the mountains, the process will be reversed. You are now lowering in elevation. You are warming up and drying out, so you are no longer producing snow (or rain).

---

[3] From a technical standpoint, the measurement for fluffy or heavy snow is its percentage of *water content*. The concept of water content is simple. If you measure the volume of snow, and then melt it and measure the volume of water it produces, the ratio of water to snow is the water content. As a rough rule of thumb, under 8% water content is light snow, 8 to 12% is average snow, and over 12% is heavy snow. Colorado winter-time storms tend to be under 8%, while spring-time storms are often over 10%. To put these numbers into perspective, manmade snow from snowmaking machines is roughly 25% water content.

Why are you warming up as you descend the back side of the mountains? Remember from Chapter 1, the first principle is that it is colder the higher you go in elevation. Well, the reverse is true so as you descend you warm up. And, as also pointed out in Chapter 1, the second principle is that warm air holds more water than cold air. So, you as the cloud will stop snowing when you descend and warm up so you can hold that moisture without letting it go. Basically, you as the cloud are going through the same process as the cold wet outside air that is warmed by a house furnace and then feels warm and dry inside the house.

This is the next major concept to understand, the ***precipitation shadow***. To the east (remember winds usually blow from west to east) of most major mountain ranges are precipitation shadows, where there simply is far less snow and rain than on the west side of the mountain range. The clouds produced precipitation as they rose over the peaks. But when they lower on the other side of the mountain, not only have the clouds used up some of their moisture, but they are also warming up and thus not continuing to produce precipitation. As such – when it's raining in Seattle, it's usually dry in all the eastern parts of Washington – such as Spokane, Ellensburg, and Yakima. (Don't worry, I'll end the discussion of Washington and get you to Colorado soon – I just wanted to walk you through your entire life as a cloud up to the point you are done snowing in Colorado.) The concept of a precipitation shadow is critical – as you'll see later – it's why Vail gets much less snow when the winds are blowing from the east and Echo Mountain gets much less snow when the winds are blowing from the west.

YOUR SECOND SNOWFALL (UTAH)

As a cloud, you meander your way towards the southeast from the Cascade Mountains of Washington until you wind up closing in on Utah.[4] This will

---

[4]   As you head southeast from Washington to Utah, you will cross the **Great Basin**. The only reason I mention the name "the Great Basin" is because forecasters love to describe weather patterns as being over "the Great Basin" even though you'll almost never hear anyone else refer to that area as the Great Basin. What is the Great Basin? It's the area constituting most of Nevada, some of Utah,

often take you a day and a half or so to do, but you move at whatever pace you like. You'll certainly move slower than the speed of cars on a traffic free interstate highway, but you're still moving at a decent clip.

As you haven't had to rise much before hitting the great Wasatch Range in Utah, you have not been producing much snow. But all of that is about to change. You may pick up a little moisture as you pass over the Great Salt Lake, and indeed you've been picking up a little moisture here and there from streams and the ground as you've been travelling. Now, the winds are blowing you up and over the Wasatch Mountains of Utah, and the process repeats itself again. If you are now following I-80, you'll have to go over Parley's Summit at 7,120', and you'll have to go even higher if you're going up over either of the Cottonwood Canyons. Orographic lifting means you'll dump snow on the lucky skiers at Alta, Snowbird, and the other Utah Resorts. Unlike when you were fresh off the Pacific Ocean and dumped heavy wet snow on the Cascade Mountains of Washington, (i.e., maritime snow), you are now 700 or more miles inland. That means you're further from the warm ocean, so the temperatures are lower, and you are producing lighter snow than before. The snow that falls in Utah, and many similar regions at the same longitude, is called ***intermountain snow***. It's lighter and fluffier than maritime snow, but not yet as light and fluffy as it'll get in Colorado.

Once past the summits of the mountains of Utah, you again descend in elevation (becoming warmer). Therefore, you will once again become stingy as a snow producer while continuing your path to Colorado. And now, although your path has already been a bit unusual (bear with me, I am using your journey to illustrate concepts more than to describe how any particular air parcel actually moves), we'll assume that you'll barrel down I-70 in Colorado. And yes, please suspend disbelief that a cloud will exactly follow an interstate highway. It will help illustrate the process.

---

and a bit of California and Oregon, where none of the water flows into an ocean. Basically, think of everything from Squaw Valley to Snowbird as the Great Basin.

Your Third Snowfall (Colorado!)

Welcome to Colorful Colorado. After a long time of relatively lower elevation travel – through Grand Junction, Glenwood Springs, and Eagle, you're about to hit Arrowhead (at the bottom of Beaver Creek) and start climbing up first over Beaver Creek and then over Vail.[5] So, with orographic lifting you start dumping snow, and this snow will fall in copious quantities on Beaver Creek and Vail. You will keep snowing as you ascend Vail Pass (10,662').

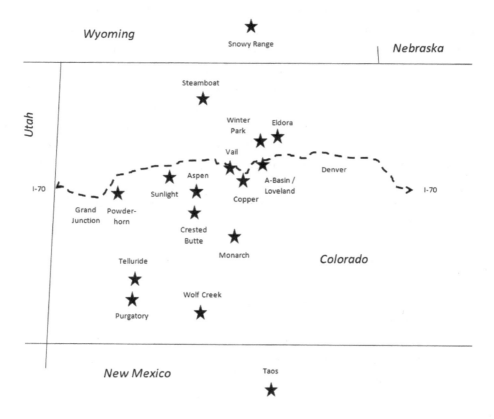

---

[5] Of course, in real life the clouds would be producing snow at Powderhorn first, Sunlight second, and only then at Beaver Creek. However, as in this illustration you the lone cloud are headed straight down I-70, so I thought I'd keep it simple.

The cold and low-density snow you are now producing is technically called **continental snow**. However, skiers call this snow by countless names, such as fluffy snow, blower powder, dry powder, white smoke, snorkel powder, cold smoke, diamond dust, etc. Whatever you call it, it is good.

Why is Colorado so amazing? Two reasons. First, as a general rule, the further one gets from the comparatively warm ocean in the winter, the colder it gets. You the cloud are now over a thousand miles from the warm Pacific Ocean. Second, as you're at the highest elevations you've been on your whole trip so far, you are the coldest that you've been. This cold is essential to producing the light fluffy powder.

It's easy to forget how high Colorado is. (For clarity, I'm referring to elevation here, not weed.) Colorado is the highest contiguous state in the nation. Roughly three-quarters of the land in the United States that is above 10,000 feet is located in Colorado. Of all the ski areas in the United States, eight of the ten highest ski areas in elevation are in Colorado, with the other two in northern New Mexico (which from a snow and powder perspective, is for all intents and purposes the same as Colorado.) So, we get some of the best powder snow in the world.

Back to you as a cloud. You may cause a blinding snowstorm by the time you reach the top of Vail Pass, but then you'll start barreling down the east side of Vail Pass and lighten up just a bit before you hit the next mountain – Copper Mountain, which starts the orographic lift yet again. As you descend in elevation along I-70 beyond Copper Mountain, you'll warm up and thus dry up a bit more. This is what locals call the **Dillon Donut** – the comparative lack of snow around the town of Dillon compared to the surrounding peaks. But you are about to face a new obstacle of stunning heights atop the Continental Divide – Loveland Pass (11,991').[6] This will cause even greater orographic lifting and thus produce even more snow.

---

[6]   And yes, you picky readers, I-70 doesn't actually go over Loveland Pass. Rather, I-70 goes under Loveland Pass one mountain to the north via the Eisenhower Tunnel. But you're missing the point. You are a cloud. You can't fit in the Eisenhower Tunnel.

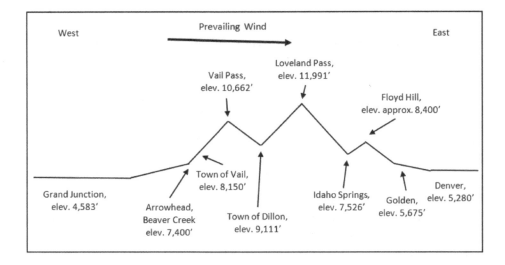

It's hardly surprising that you still have lots of snow left in you to dump snow over Loveland Pass. Notice how your journey started ascending the 3,015' Snoqualmie Pass in Washington, then the higher 7,120' Parley's Summit in Utah, and then the higher 10,662' Vail Pass in Colorado, and now you have to make it over 11,991' to scale Loveland Pass.

Now it's time to introduce the last key concept in snow production, the **_spillover effect_**. When you hit the highest point (for example, Loveland Pass), it's not as if you stop snowing instantly as you start to descend the other side. Quite the contrary, you will continue to produce massive amounts of snow for the next few miles before your elevation drops significantly. But then, as your elevation starts really dropping, you'll warm up and stop producing snow.

This is why when you (the real you, not the cloud you) are driving towards Denver from the Eisenhower Tunnel in a snowstorm, it's usually snowing like mad at the Loveland Ski Area exit as you leave the Eisenhower Tunnel, but it is dry by the time you pass the towns of Silver Plume and Georgetown. Loveland Ski Area, just east of the Continental Divide, is well within the spillover effect, but Silver Plume and Georgetown are not. So, Loveland will get pummeled by the snow, but Silver Plume and Georgetown will not. Often, the snow will suddenly stop at the Bakersville exit. One mile to the west of that exit is still within the spillover effect and one mile to the east of the exit is well beyond the spillover effect and into the precipitation shadow.

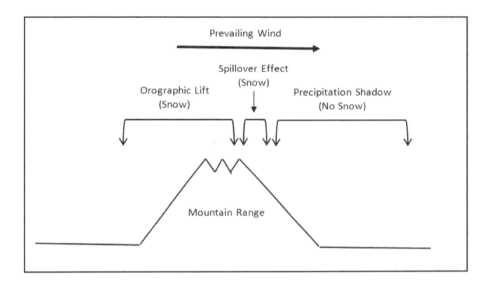

The importance of the spillover effect cannot be overstated. Many of Colorado's snowiest ski areas are in the spillover effect area – think of Breckenridge, Loveland, Monarch, and Wolf Creek. All of them sit facing east just beyond a snowy peak or ridge, and all get amazing snow. Now, as discussed in Chapter 19, wind transport of snow also helps each of these ski areas to get additional snow, but none of them would have their great snow without the spillover effect.

Your journey as a cloud will continue downhill past Idaho Springs, and if you're feeling like pestering the drivers on their way back from the mountains, you might eke out a little snow as you climb to the Floyd Hill part of I-70. But then you'll stop producing snow as you head towards Denver and the plains. Lowering in elevation, you will be funneled into the canyons (like Clear Creek Canyon and Boulder Canyon). Like a river going down a narrow stretch, these narrow canyons will cause you to speed up (i.e., the winds will increase). This is part of the reason why Boulder and Golden are so windy.

Alright, so we've covered orographic lifting following the prevailing wind — that is one blowing from west to east. But what happens when the wind switches direction? Let's address this question next.

Chapter 3

Imagine You Are a Cloud (Round Two): Turn Around and Go From East to West

At this point you might be thinking, how are there ever big powder days at Eldora or Hidden Valley (the former a popular ski area and the latter a popular backcountry spot, both well east of the continental divide)? Both mountains have plenty of powder days, yet they're getting into the precipitation shadow beyond the continental divide. Well, if you live in the front range of Colorado, have you ever noticed that on maybe a dozen days a year, you can smell the hog farms from the eastern plains? Normally, you can't smell them as the wind typically blows from the west. But, now and again, you can smell them. And, that usually means that it will snow the next day, because the winds are now blowing from the east. The smell of hog farms (or the "smell of money" as the ranchers often call it), is also the smell of snow. There's a storm blowing in from the east.

When a storm causes winds to blow from the east, the process of orographic lifting comes into play again, but from the opposite direction. So, if you are now a cloud coming in from the east, you will produce some snow in Denver, more in Golden as you start to climb, and far more at the top of Floyd Hill because, once again, you are cooling down, which causes you to produce more snow. Let's stick with the assumption that you as a cloud will once again follow I-70, just heading from the east towards the west this time. You'll dump over Floyd Hill, but lower a bit in elevation as you head by Idaho Springs. Drivers stuck in these storms can attest to the misery of climbing Floyd Hill, with the "surprise" of typically better roads as they descend in elevation towards Idaho Springs. Idaho Springs is like Dillon in Chapter 2 (remember the Dillon Donut) – it's lower elevation than the surrounding peaks, meaning it has less snow than I-70 on either side of it. As you climb up towards Loveland Ski Area and Loveland Pass, once again orographic lifting will cause heavy snows, but beyond the spillover effect a couple of miles to the west of Loveland Pass, your descent in elevation will cause your snow to peter out.

These storms where the winds are blowing from the east are often referred to as **upslope storms**, though this is a purely Colorado term. Mention an upslope storm to a meteorologist not from Colorado, and he or she will think of a different weather phenomenon. And, although there are always exceptions, upslope storms tend to drop heavier snow (i.e., higher moisture content snow) than storms coming from the west. This happens for several reasons. First, the storms where the winds blow from the east in the front range tend to originate from a warmer direction (the southwest). They often form near Hawaii, travel from the southwest towards Colorado, and switch wind direction as they start to get over the plains. Second, as the storms are switching directions on this journey, they often pull moisture from the Gulf of Mexico as well as the warmer parts of the Pacific Ocean. You as the cloud in an upslope storm were partially born in the Pacific Ocean, but also partially born in the warm Gulf of Mexico. Third, and perhaps most importantly, these storms occur more commonly in the warmer fall or spring months as opposed to during the heart of winter. (If you're confused why the wind is coming from the east and south, be patient. This will be explained in Chapter 4.)

Unfortunately, these upslope storms often do not reach quite the same lofty elevations. Their winds tend not to be as strong – after all, their winds blowing from the east are fighting the normal prevailing westerly winds. With weaker winds, you as the cloud may never make it past Floyd Hill. You may just create snowy roads on Floyd Hill, but not create snowy conditions at the higher elevation ski areas that you just don't have the energy to reach. Conversely, if the winds are easterly not only at the ground level are also easterly much higher in the atmosphere, you may be able to produce a little snow all the way to Vail Pass – though you've already dropped most of your moisture at the higher elevation Loveland Pass (11,991') than the lower elevation and further distant Vail Pass (10,662').

For what it's worth, the same thing can be true from the more typical storm coming from the west. In such storms, sometimes the energy peters out after Vail Pass and before Loveland Pass, and other times the storm has so much energy it will still produce snow, if not that much, all the way to Denver.[7]

Notice how the wind direction is key? If the wind comes from the west, in our example, Vail gets hammered and Floyd Hill is dry. And, if the wind comes from the east, in our example, Floyd Hill gets hammered but Vail stays dry.

Wind direction is critical to hunting powder in Colorado. Wind direction is one of the first items to look at in order to guess (um, I mean forecast) where it will snow.

The mountain topography of my beloved Berthoud Pass (11,307') tends to get the most snow from northwest winds. Westerly winds will produce snow at Berthoud Pass. Because it is within the spillover effect for upslope storms, even easterly winds mean snow for Berthoud Pass. However, due

---

[7] One complicating factor to your journey as a cloud (and there are always complicating factors) is that you bounce. I'm not making this up. As a parcel of air descends just beyond a high mountain, it will literally bounce off the lower terrain and rise up again further downwind. The air parcel will continue this bouncing up and down as it gets further from the main mountain. (To visualize the air mass' movement, think of someone dribbling a basketball down the basketball court, and then letting the ball bounce on its own. It will bounce in smaller and smaller bounces as it makes its way down the basketball court.) On the upswings in this bouncing, the air parcel gets colder forming clouds and occasionally a little more snow. The amount of snow the bounces produce, if any, is small enough to not be worth considering when you're forecasting snow.

Forecasters confusingly call this vertical movement of air parcels **gravity waves** – though "dribbling" would probably be a better term.

to the particular topography of the mountains by Berthoud Pass, when the wind blows from the northwest, it will just dump at Berthoud Pass.

And, slight differences in the wind pattern and storm energy will make some drainages near Berthoud Pass have more snow than others. Why? Because the size of the geographic feature that causes orographic lifting can be quite small. Studies have shown that a hill as small as 150 feet tall can produce orographic lifting. So, terrain variations between the various drainages of Berthoud Pass can each create their own unique orographic lifting.

How important is orographic lifting? Ironically, if you pick up the average weather book and read about precipitation, orographic lifting is usually relegated to a mere side point. For an extreme example, probably the most popular mass market American book on weather is Jack William's *The Weather Book*. While otherwise excellent, this book does not even mention orographic lifting.[8] Similarly, the major introductory (and excellent) textbook on meteorology, C. Donald Ahrens' *Essentials of Meteorology*, spends only two pages out of the nearly 500-page textbook on orographic lifting.[9] Outside of mountainous regions, folks don't care about orographic lifting. For most of the country, it doesn't snow or rain because of orographic lifting.

But here in Colorado (because we have lots of big mountains), the key snow producer is orographic lifting. How key? One of the first large-scale studies of winter storm precipitation in Colorado shows a six-fold increase of precipitation between Grand Junction and Vail Pass. In other words, over 80% of the snowfall at Vail Pass results primarily from orographic lifting. Orographic lifting is the main show and everything else are just side points.

---

[8] The lack of a reference to this key topic leads to a chart in the book that every Colorado skier would laugh at. It shows snowfall variation throughout the United States where the top category is over 60 inches annually. So, both Golden and Wolf Creek fall into the same category – over 60 inches. So does most of New York State. Somehow, I think that skiers do actually care about the difference between 60 inches and over 400 inches of snow annually.

[9] In contrast to this indifference, 7News meteorologist Mike Nelson's wonderful book on Colorado weather, *Colorado Weather Almanac*, wisely and literally starts the book with orographic lifting (though not using the term), discussing it for five pages in the very first part of the very first chapter.

So, in two chapters, you've learned about far and away the most important contributor to snowfall in our fair state.

As I close out the two chapters on orographic lifting, I hope you've enjoyed your life as a cloud. Many, if not most of the key concepts of snow production have now been introduced. But you may have noticed there was a glaring omission in this chapter. If the wind normally blows from west side of the compass to the east side of the compass, why does it sometimes do a literal 180 degree turn and blow from the complete opposite direction? In other words, why doesn't the wind always blow from the same general direction? And how is this predicted?

This brings us to the second most important concept in snow production after orographic lifting – low pressure systems. Let's explore this topic next.

Chapter 4

Lows Get Skiers High: Understanding Low Pressure Systems

L et's take a step back. If orographic lifting is all that matters for snow, how does it ever snow more than a couple of inches in Denver (or the flat easterly plains of Colorado)? Everything we've discussed up to this point relates to orographic lifting, which is the most important snow producer in Colorado. However, it does still snow (albeit far less) in non-mountainous places like Denver and the easterly plains of Colorado. What's going on?

Snowfall is produced in five ways. First, is orographic lifting, which you are now an expert in. Second, snow is produced by low pressure. Third, snow is produced by jet streaks. Fourth, snow is produced by fronts. And fifth, snow is produced by convection. Neatly, all five methods (orographic lifting, low pressure, jet streaks, fronts, and convection) involve the exact same mechanism — water vapor being lifted in elevation until it's cold enough to snow. The different methods just differ in what causes the cloud to lift.

Of the remaining four methods, low pressure is the second most important one for the big front range storms (which is where I live) — but not as important for many of Colorado's other mountainous areas. Low pressure is so critical for my neck of the woods not just because of low pressure's innate snow producing quality. Rather, while low pressure does create snow on its own (low pressure creates lift that creates snow), low pressure has the most significant impact in altering wind directions during snowfall. As we've already discussed, winds fuel orographic lifting snow production. Low pressure can drive winds and snow from directions other than the western half of the compass – radically altering the areas that orographic lifting favors.

Let's start with some background to understand the concept of low pressure (and its evil cousin high pressure) by thinking globally, starting at the equator. Then, let's add into the mix global wind patterns. With these big picture items addressed, we can finally return to thinking locally about low pressures in Colorado. And if you're the impatient type or don't care about the larger concepts, feel free to skip ahead to the Colorado focused portion of this chapter.

THINK GLOBALLY: LOW AND HIGH PRESSURE ON A GLOBAL SCALE

Imagine you are a cloud at the equator. Okay, I know you don't want to be near the equator because there's almost no skiing near the equator, but suck it up for this thought experiment.

So, you are a cloud near the ground at the equator. The sun is directly above your head, and that makes you really hot. What does air do when it's hot? It expands and rises.[10] That's how a hot air balloon works. So, you rise high up into the air. With you gone from the ground at the equator, and now high up in the sky, something must fill the gap that you left. Cooler fresh air that was north and south of the equator has to spill in. But this fresh air that spills into the location that you just left will in turn warm under the hot equatorial sun and rise. So more cooler fresh air must head in to replace it, which is likewise warming up.

Meanwhile, you are rising. Hot air rising expands. So, you as the hot air begin to cool down as you rise because you've been expanding. Remember, air cools as it rises. Although you are at the equator, as you're rising higher into the atmosphere you are cooling off. And what happens when rising air

---

[10] Hot air rises because when air is heated it expands. When it expands, it becomes less dense than the air around it. And like a rubber-ducky rises to the top of the water in a bathtub, the less dense hot air rises compared to the more dense colder air around it.

cools? It creates rain (near the equator) or snow (when further away from the equator). The Amazon rain forest is right on the equator. That's why it's the Amazon rain forest and not the Amazon desert. The hot sun at the equator causes lifting, which in turn causes rain. It's a bit counterintuitive that the hottest areas on earth are usually not right at the equator as the heat causes lift that causes rain on the equator.

Now remember how all the fresh air was replacing / filling in the place you left because you were rising? That fresh air is now rising behind you, pushing against you high up in the sky. So, you have to go somewhere. Where do you go? You are being pushed by the new air rising away from the equator – so you are headed, high in the sky, in the direction of the poles.

All is well and good on your trip towards the north pole (and towards places with ski areas) except for one little problem. As you start your slow journey as a cloud northward, the darn earth is spinning! And it's spinning fast. Literally, the earth is spinning beneath you. To an observer on the ground, your cloud journey would not look like it's headed straight north, but rather as you get further from the equator, it would look like you are curving to the right. (This is the Coriolis Effect, and we'll discuss it in more depth soon.) You'll never make it to the north pole, and in any event as you head north the sun is lower in the sky so you're getting colder. So, you'll start to sink because you're now colder. And what happens when air descends? It compresses, so it heats up and dries out.

It turns out that you'll descend back towards the Earth at very roughly 30 degrees latitude either north or south of the equator.[11] Descending air

---

[11] Why do I say "very roughly" in the sentence? Remember that as the earth's tilt relative to the sun changes, the sun's most direct heating on earth changes. During the spring and fall equinox the sun is directly overhead at the equator, at the summer solstice it is directly overhead at the Tropic of Cancer, and at the winter solstice it is directly overhead at the Tropic of Capricorn. So, that changes the relative location of the highs and lows described in this section. Moreover, ocean location, ocean currents, land location, and land topography all play into the average location of the highs and lows – so this description (like almost all concepts in weather) must necessarily be an oversimplification.

warms up and dries out. This, not coincidentally, is the latitude of the Sahara Desert in the northern hemisphere and the desert-like Australian Outback in the southern hemisphere. Both the Sahara Desert and the Outback exist because they're places where the air is always descending from above. Descending air is warm and dry – the opposite of ascending air.

Once you've descended onto the Sahara (or the Outback), more air is descending above you, pushing you out of the way. So, at this point you are being pushed back towards the equator. The equator, after all, is where your journey began.[12]

---

[12] The same circulation pattern is occurring, but the other way, at the poles. The poles get very little sun. So, the air is cool over the poles and it sinks. As we discussed, descending air is dry. This is why central Antarctica is a desert, albeit covered with ice. It rarely snows near the south pole, just like it rarely rains in the Sahara. And Santa Clause, on the north pole, rarely sees snow. So don't believe all the pictures of Santa's workshop under freshly fallen snow you see on Christmas Cards. The high pressure over the poles from the sinking air forces the bottom layer of air to head towards the equator. The air goes from the poles along the surface until roughly 60 degrees latitude. At this point, as it is warming, it climbs, gets cold, snows, and heads back higher in the atmosphere back towards the pole. And sure enough, where is this 60 degree latitude line? Roughly the latitude of Anchorage. So, this circulation is causing some of the snow at Alyeska Ski Area. And more importantly for our purposes, it is generating many of the low pressure systems near the Aleutian Islands of Alaska, which will eventually make their way to Colorado to produce snow.

The two circulations in the northern hemisphere – one at the tropics and one at the poles – forces the air in the mid-latitudes to circulate as well. The mid-latitudes are between 30 and 60 degrees. Baseline Road in Boulder is exactly at the 40th degree latitude, so Colorado sits right in the middle of the mid-latitudes. The air in the midlatitudes is being dragged upwards at 60 degrees and dragged downwards at 30 degrees due to the two other circulation patterns, so the mid-latitudes end up having its own circulation. (If you were curious why winds blow in from west to east in the mid-latitudes, it's because of the atmospheric circulation in the midlatitudes from the high pressure at 30 degrees latitude (think tip of Texas) to low pressure at 60 degrees latitude (think Anchorage), but is forced to the right by the Coriolis effect.)

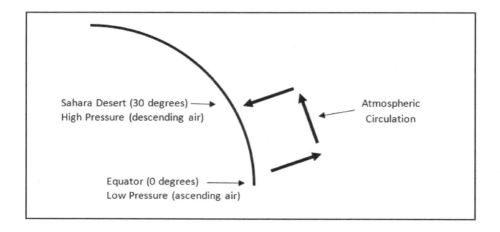

Why did we just spend half a dozen paragraphs discussing an air circulation pattern? It's not just so you understand why it's wet in the Amazon rain forest at the equator and dry at the Sahara Desert at 30 degrees latitude. It's because this discussion introduces two key concepts. First, you must visualize the atmosphere in three dimensions. Second, whether you know it or not, you just learned what a high pressure system is – that's where you were being forced down by vertical air above you at the Sahara. And you learned

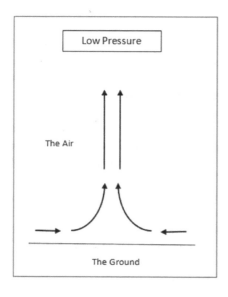

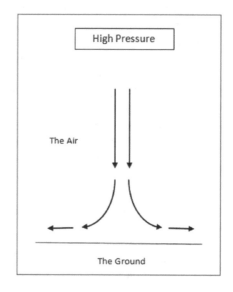

about what low pressure system is – that's where you were at the equator and rising as other air moved into your location. Pressure systems are about vertical movement. A **high pressure system** is the vertical movement of air downwards. And it tends to be warmer. A **low pressure system** is the vertical movement of air upwards. And it tends to be cooler (both literally and figuratively).

Okay, frankly there is a third concept that this discussion starts to introduce, which is that the atmosphere is bloody complicated. Numerous forces (temperature, pressure, density, rotation, etc.) are all acting at once – some operating in concert with each other and others operating against each other.

WINDS AND THE CORIOLIS EFFECT

Let's add one more concept that you already intuitively understand. Winds blow from areas of high concentration (i.e., high pressure) to low concentration (i.e., low pressure). The movement of gases from high concentration to low concentration is universal, and I always explain the concept when teaching avalanche classes with a crude analogy. Let's say, as I'm teaching the avalanche class, I let a big fart rip out. Initially there will be a high concentration of smelly molecules near me, up front, but none of the students will smell it immediately. Then slowly the smell molecules move from an area of high concentration, near my butt, to a lower concentration out towards the first row of desks. Soon the students in the first row will smell my fart but the students in the further back rows won't have smelled it yet. But the fact is that the smell molecule concentration may now be equal between where I am and where the first row is, but it's still a higher concentration than the back row. So, the smell molecules continue to travel to the area of lower concentration, the back row, until the whole room can smell my fart. Unappetizing example? Sorry. The education goal was met. You'll never forget the fact that gases and liquids move from areas of high concentration to areas of low concentration.

One tricky thing to remember with regards to winds and pressure systems is that the winds don't blow straight out of a high pressure or straight into a low pressure. I've briefly mentioned this already. The spin of the earth deflects the wind. How does it do that?

Imagine you are an alien astronaut who plans to land your flying saucer close to the north pole. As you're coming in for your landing, the earth below you will be spinning counterclockwise. And, if you are the dumbfounded earthling staring up at the flying saucer trying to land near the North Pole, it will look like the flying saucer is heading clockwise above you as it comes in for its landing. In reality, the earthling is the one who is spinning, not the alien. But if you were to draw a map of how the alien's flying saucer is coming in, it'll look like its trajectory is curving. And that's the whole point. It's not that the wind is rotating above us on earth. Rather, we are rotating below it. This is the **Coriolis Effect**. And if you're an earthling at the South Pole watching a flying saucer try to land on the South Pole, it will appear to rotate the opposite way because you are rotating the opposite way.[13]

Wait, you might say, how can I be rotating the opposite way if I'm on the same globe? The answer is because you are standing literally upside down compared with the person on the north pole. Think of two ants crawling on opposite sides of a basketball – each one would think the one on the other side is upside down. This is why constellations appear upside down from the Southern Hemisphere. I know the first time I saw Orion and Taurus upside down while in South Africa, I knew what they taught us in school must be correct – the earth is, in fact, not flat. It's a crazy concept if you think about it, as the earth certainly looks flat to me as I go about my daily life. But it's not flat, and the constellations over the equator look upside down from the southern hemisphere.

The Coriolis Effect is only noticeable over longer time scales – you watch that flying saucer come in for an hour at the pole, and it will be quite noticeable from beginning to end – while the rotation will barely be visible

---

[13] The Coriolis Force disappears at the equator, which is why hurricanes never form on the equator or cross the equator. If you want more information on why this is true, as it would take too long for my feeble brain to explain, and in any event I'd hate to put figures into a footnote, please check out the further reading recommendations in Appendix F.

if you watch it for only 30 seconds. Because of this, toilets do not flush the opposite way in the Southern Hemisphere.

Trust me, having seen the Simpson's episode where they say toilets flush the other way in Australia, I've looked carefully at which way the toilet flushes on every continent on earth. I can tell you from my own eyes, they don't spin the opposite way in Australia, South Africa, Chile, or Antarctica. The time scale and size scale are too small in a toilet for the Coriolis effect to make a difference.

But what isn't too small when it comes to size and time scale? The moving air above you. So, now we're ready for the key point.

The Coriolis Effect (in the northern hemisphere) forces the air out of the high pressure area in a clockwise direction. And, it forces air into the low pressure in a counterclockwise direction. In fact, the Coriolis Effect is so strong, if it weren't for the friction of the air against the earth, the winds would simply blow perpendicular to the direction of the center of the low.

Forecasters sometimes call low pressure areas *cyclones* and sometimes call high pressure areas *anticyclones*. As if two words for the same thing isn't bad enough, the names get even more confusing as cyclones circulate counterclockwise, and anticyclones rotate clockwise. Okay, that's really confusing language. Let's stick with low pressure and high pressure for the purposes of this book.[14]

---

[14]   If it helps, Chapter 16 has a chart showing the various synonyms for low pressure and high pressure. Since I've already mentioned the alternate term cyclone, it's worth mentioning that a cyclone is not a tornado or a hurricane, though both tornadoes and hurricanes are formed from a low pressure, a/k/a a cyclone. Nevertheless, people sometimes associate the word "cyclone" with a tornado or hurricane. The media has taken advantage of that in making scary sounding news reports of *bomb cyclones*. A bomb cyclone is simply a low pressure area (i.e. a cyclone) where the pressure drops over roughly 26 millibars or more in 24 hours. That's a significant drop and means a powerful storm. While a bomb cyclone can produce big snow, it doesn't usually produce nearly as much as a cut-off low, discussed in Chapter 8. And it produces nothing like the snow when a storm combines with orographic lifting. The media never mentions that in the sensational reporting on bomb cyclones. And surprise,

ACT LOCALLY: WHAT LOW PRESSURE SYSTEMS MEANS FOR COLORADO SKIERS

If your eyes glazed over while reading about the big picture, start paying close attention again. As we look at Colorado, this will make a big difference for powder. There are three key concepts to keep in mind when it comes to low pressures.

First, air heads into a low pressure area and rises as it gets close to the center of the low pressure. What happens when moist air rises? Rising air cools down creating snow. So, low pressure is good. It causes snow.

Second, low pressure systems tend to be weaker over the mountains and stronger over the plains. (We'll discuss this more in Chapter 24.) So, they tend to disproportionally impact the mountainous areas adjacent to the plains.

Third, low pressure creates counterclockwise winds. And high pressure creates clockwise winds. Because of this, it most often snows in my house in Golden when the low pressure is in the southern part of Colorado. The winds are rotating counterclockwise (which in some instances can even pull moisture in from as far away as the Gulf of Mexico) and the rotation of the low to the south of my house causes the winds to blow into the side of Lookout Mountain in Golden from the east or southeast. That air then rises (here because of the orographic lifting from Lookout Mountain more than the lifting from the low pressure), and if the air is moist, it will snow. This happens more often than one might expect, because the Rocky Mountains literally create low pressure systems. As you're probably already overloaded with concepts in this chapter, I'll wait to Chapter 24 to explain how and why the Rocky Mountains create low pressure systems.

This also raises the important point that during a storm, the wind isn't blowing from just one direction throughout Colorado. If the low pressure

---

surprise, the media never wants to use the technical term for the creation of the supposed bomb cyclone, an explosive cyclogenesis. I'd guess calling it a bomb cyclone just sounds far more scary than an explosive cyclogenesis. And, explosive cyclogenesis does sound more like something that happens after eating spoiled food.

is centered in the southeastern part of Colorado, the wind in Golden and at Eldora will blow from the east or northeast. But, for Monarch Mountain, the wind will be blowing from the northwest. One storm, multiple wind directions.

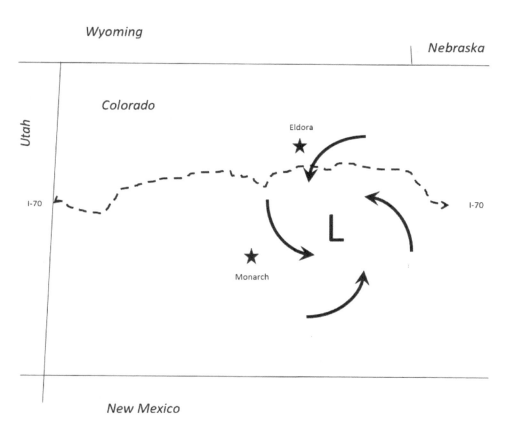

High pressure systems can also produce some snow in Colorado. Wait, I can hear you cry, I thought high pressure causes warm dry weather (think of the Sahara Desert)? True, but high pressure also creates winds from atypical directions that can cause orographic lifting.

Let's go back to my house on the side of Lookout Mountain in Golden and revisit the more intuitive low pressure system. If a low pressure is to the southeast of my house in Golden (let's say centered to the east of Pueblo), its counterclockwise winds will be pushing moisture from the east towards my house and Lookout Mountain. As the air hits Lookout Mountain and is forced to lift (and adiabatic cooling occurs) – voila, snow. But, if that low pressure instead is centered over Greeley, to the northeast of my house, that low pressure will prevent snow. Why? Because the counterclockwise air heading into the low pressure is coming in from the northwest, and as it descends from the mountain heights to my house it will be warming (that is, adiabatic warming occurs) and thus will be less likely to produce snow. So, a low pressure can prevent snow in a mountain environment as much as create it, depending upon its location.

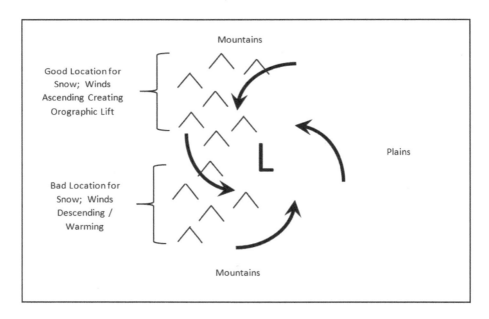

A high pressure works the same way. If there is a high pressure over Greeley, the air flows out of it clockwise. That means that warm air is coming at my house on the side of Lookout Mountain from the east. And, as it rises to get over Lookout Mountain, it cools and will snow. After all, it's all about the wind. So, a high pressure, if combined with orographic lifting, can even cause snow, albeit usually not as much as low pressure.

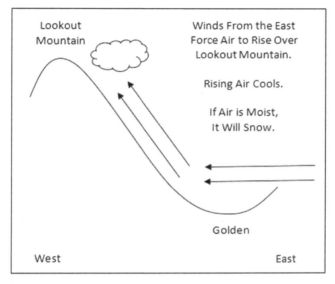

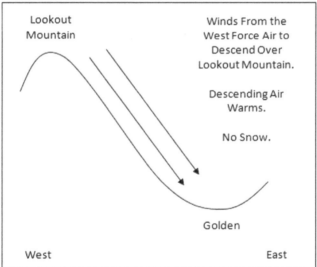

Let's summarize. Low pressure systems not only lift air, but they also create counterclockwise winds, which cause upslope storms. I like low pressure
systems.

Chapter 5

Imagine You Are a Balloonist: Understanding How Jet Streaks Create Snow

Two down, three to go. As I've explained, snowfall is produced in five ways. First, there is orographic lifting, which we discussed in Chapters 2 and 3. Second, there is low pressure, which we just covered in Chapter 4. So, let's take a look at the third method – the elusive jet streaks.

I use the term *elusive* because jet streaks are perhaps more difficult to understand than any other atmospheric method of snow production. And to make matters worse, while weather models (see Chapters 10 and 11) do a decent job in predicting where jet streaks will occur, weather models do a very poor job in predicting how much snow any particular jet streak will produce.

Before we begin our discussion of jet streaks, let's take a step back and talk first about the related concept of the jet stream.

QUICK BACKGROUND ON THE JET STREAM

As discussed in Chapter 4, the sun heats the earth more the closer one gets to the equator than the poles. This is obvious. Hawaii is warmer than Alaska. Duh, big red truck.

The regions near the equator tend to stay warm year-round while the regions near the poles tend to stay cold year around. Their battle ground is in the temperate regions (where Colorado is located). The dividing line between the cold polar air and the warmer mid-latitude air is largely defined by the upper-level *jet stream*. (Okay, it's more complicated than this – it always is – but it's better to be 90% accurate and understandable than 100% accurate and unintelligible.)

The jet stream is a band of intense wind in the upper atmosphere that runs very roughly from west to east around the globe. It's conveniently called the jet stream as it's at the altitude at which jets fly – and can rapidly speed up a trip heading from west to east on a plane.

Why does the jet stream exist as this boundary between the colder polar air and the warmer mid-latitude air? The pressure difference between the different temperature air masses creates winds (remember that warm air is less dense than cold air). The spinning of the earth (remember the Coriolis Effect) causes the winds to wind their way around the globe from west to east in the mid-latitudes.

Thought Exercise, Trying to Travel the Jet Stream in a Balloon

At this point, you're probably sick of imagining yourself as a cloud. So, let's imagine something a tad more realistic – though please don't try this at home. Imagine in this chapter that your sport of choice is ballooning, not skiing. One morning you wake up and think – the jet stream moves fast, why don't I travel across the globe (or maybe just the United States) with my balloon on the jet stream?

Now I'm no balloonist, so take my thoughts with a grain of salt, but I wouldn't suggest you try this for three reasons. First, while the jet stream does move at an extraordinary clip in some places, there's a lot less air at the elevation of the jet stream. So, the winds at that elevation will hardly push your balloon as effectively as winds closer to the surface. Second, as there's not much air at the height of the jet stream, you'll need oxygen. And of the little air there is – roughly 20 to 30% of the air at sea level – the air will be awfully cold. Third, the jet stream is not like a stream of water on land. It does not follow a fixed course that you can put a raft into and float downstream. Rather, its location, speed, and strength are constantly in flux – so one day it will blow you in the proper direction (say west) at a good speed, but the next day it will suddenly be blowing you in a not as great direction (say north) or have simply moved to some other location.

In fact, if you want an example of how poor of a plan it is to ride the jet stream via balloon, look no further than World War II. As the United States is downstream of Japan via the jet stream, the Japanese came up with the idea that they could attack the United States by bombs carried by unmanned balloons riding the jet stream. So, Japan sent more than 6,000 unmanned balloons carrying bombs along the jet stream to rain down in terror over the mainland of the United States. How successful was this bombing campaign? Well, I bet you've heard of Pearl Harbor. Airplanes work. On the other hand, I bet you've never heard of the jet stream balloon bombs until you read this paragraph. The fact that you never heard about this attempted attack demonstrates just how ineffective the attack was. Don't trust the jet stream to carry your balloon.

But let's set aside facts for the sake of a hopefully clever teaching tool, and in this Chapter, let's assume you are a balloonist riding the jet stream. Now before you begin your balloon journey along the jet stream, there are a few important items about the jet stream to remember.

First, if you want to ride the jet stream, plan to do this during the wintertime, not the summertime. Why? The jet stream isn't stationary. Like many bird species, the jet stream migrates north over the summer and migrates back south over the winter. This makes sense, as the polar air mass expands over the winter and contracts over the summer. During the summer, the jet stream is over Canada and never gets as far south as Colorado. However, as the northern hemisphere cools down as winter approaches, the jet stream (marking the boundary between cold air and warm air) veers south and is often over Colorado.

The jet stream is also stronger during the winter as compared to the summer because there's a greater temperature difference in the winter than the summer. This is easy to remember. Detroit is cold and Dallas is hot in the winter, but during the summer, both Detroit and Dallas are hot. Temperature differences create pressure differences (warm air is less dense than cold air), and pressure differences drive the winds.

Second, if you tried to find and ride the jet stream in your balloon using one of those maps of the jet stream they show during the weather portion of television news, you'd be out of luck. You'd be out of luck because the jet stream's actual pattern looks nothing at all like those silly maps.[15] Rather, and unfortunately, it is far more complicated and amorphous. The jet stream doesn't have a constant width. It doesn't have a constant strength. And it meanders in an ever-changing wave pattern up and down. Indeed, it's a shame it's called the jet stream at all because that conjures up images of a river or stream, which is not a fair comparison. It should be called the jet current – as people who spend time at beaches know there are places where currents on average are stronger or weaker, but the strength of the current at any one location is constantly changing, just like the speed and location of the jet stream is constantly changing.

With all of this in mind, let us finally start the thought experiment balloon ride. On one particular day, in order to follow the jet stream, perhaps your balloon journey starts above Seattle, Washington. You may head relatively slowly in an easterly direction towards Idaho in the jet stream. Then you'll accelerate like mad to your right as you head south towards Colorado. You've just entered a jet streak, the fastest portion of the jet stream, that we'll discuss that more in a bit. Just as you're passing over Denver you're at the end of the jet streak, so you'll slow down and start to turn back to your left and head to the northeast and fly over the Great Lakes at a decent clip (but not as fast as before). Then, once past the Great Lakes and over eastern Canada, you might turn to the right (southwards again to visit northern New England) before you are out over the ocean. This is but one of a myriad of almost countless different jet stream paths that are possible over North America.

---

[15] If you want to know what the jet stream looks like right now, and assuming its winter time when you're reading this, which means that the jet stream should be more-or-less over the United States, go to https://www.spc.noaa.gov/obswx/maps/. Choose 12Z time (to keep it simple), and choose the 300 mb map (i.e., 300 millibar map). The image that you are looking at is what the jet stream looked like at 5 am today.

Speed Creates Lift, and Lift Creates Snow

At this point you might be wondering, what does the jet stream have to do with snow? And why would different parts of a balloon journey on the jet stream cause more or less snow? Well, the answer is the jet stream and its jet streaks have a huge impact on snowfall. Their longer-term patterns will be discussed in Chapter 8. On the shorter time horizon, let us start with a key concept.

Speed creates lift. Fast moving air lifts the air below it upwards. A fun simple household experiment demonstrates this proposition. Take a newspaper (if any newspapers still exist) and cut out a 1" by 10" paper rectangle. Put the 1" side right below your bottom lip, so the long end of the paper flops down in front of your chin. Now blow air above the newspaper stip. What happens may surprise you. The newspaper lifts up as you blow air above it. Why? Because by blowing air away above the newspaper strip, you've created low pressure above it. The air pressure from below the newspaper strip (where there is higher pressure) pushes the newspaper strip up. Speed creates lift. For those who are more geeky, we're talking about Bernoulli's principle, and this is the same scientific principle which forms the basis of the shape of airplane wings.

Okay, are you on board with the fact that speed creates lift? Faster moving air aloft raises air below it. Of course, it's more complicated (it's always more complicated), but the jet stream (and its faster portions, the jet streaks) create lift because of their speed.

As we learned in Chapter 1, what happens when air is lifted higher into the atmosphere? It cools down and snows. And, with enough moisture and enough lift, it can snow like mad.

Jet Streaks

So, now that we understand the basics of the jet stream and about why fast-moving air higher in the atmosphere creates lift that creates snow, let's talk about the big snow producer – jet streaks.

As already noted, the jet stream is not some continuous river of faster moving air, but rather a band of air whose precise location is constantly moving, and within the band it can move fast, slow, and curve northwards, southwards, or westwards. Don't think of it as a static and continuous river. Think of it as an ever-changing current of air.

The fastest moving segments of the jet stream are called *jet streaks*. Jet streaks, like the larger jet stream, are formed by temperature differences. Remember, temperature differences create pressure differences, and pressure differences drive wind. If you love to ski powder, you should love jet streaks, as jet streaks can produce extraordinary amounts of snow.

To visualize a jet streak, imagine that you are a balloonist (again don't try this at home), and you want to catch a ride in the jet streak. (Don't forget to bring oxygen.) Imagine the jet streak starts in Idaho and ends in Colorado. You'll have to maneuver your balloon to the proper elevation, say roughly 30,000' or the 300 millibar level in meteorology speak, so you are in the jet stream, and upwind of the jet streak itself. Your balloon will be blowing pretty fast from the northwest to the southeast as you're in the jet stream, though not yet in the jet streak. But you're about to speed up a lot more. As your balloon is about to enter this jet streak, which is called the *entrance region*, you accelerate rapidly until you are significantly exceeding one hundred miles per hour. You are now in the jet streak. You get whizzed along from southern Idaho to where the jet streak ends in Colorado. At this point, you are at the *exit region* of the jet streak, and you will decelerate as the winds will be slowing you down to a relatively calm speed of fifty or eighty miles an hour. What a ride that would be!

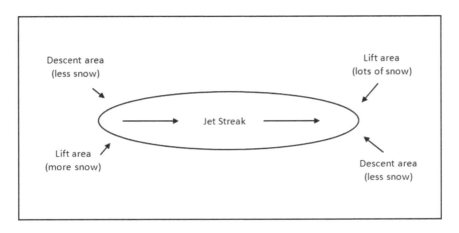

There are two portions of the jet streak that produce the most snow — the right entrance region and the left exit region. What does that mean? In your balloon voyage, if you are entering the jet streak from the right side (i.e., usually the south side), you are in the right entrance region. So, you'll be directly above a heavier snow area. And when you exit the jet streak, if you exit to the left side (i.e., usually the north side), you are in the left exit region. And this area will likewise be directly above a heavier snow area.

My advice to you is just to memorize that the land areas below the right entrance region and left exit region of the jet streak are the best spots for snow.[16] While most concepts in meteorology make intuitive sense (like air lifting over a mountain creating snow), which reduces the need for memorization, I have never found the snow producing portions of the jet streak to make intuitive sense, and memorization has proved to be much easier.

For most readers — just take my word that the right entrance and left exit regions are the biggest snow producers — and skip this paragraph. But, for the few readers who insist on knowing why it is that these two areas are the best snow producers, read on. Seriously, you're still reading this paragraph? I've warned you, skip to the next paragraph! To keep this as simple as possible, winds that are not near the surface in our part of the world tend to be geostrophic (i.e., they run parallel to the air pressure contours) because the pressure gradient force pushing the winds from higher pressure towards the lower pressure (usually northward) is balanced by the Coriolis effect pushing

---

[16] My trick for memorizing this is to visualize my car as a jet streak. My family and I usually sit in the same seats in the car, with me driving in the front left seat, my son in the back left seat, and my daughter in the back right seat. So, if my car is the jet streak, I sit by the left exit region as the car drives forward (where there's the most snow) and my daughter sits by the right entrance region (where there's the second most snow). This fits well today to help me memorize the locations, as I'm the best skier in the family and my daughter is the second-best skier in the family. When I see a jet streak in an upper atmosphere chart, I just mentally put the passenger compartment of my car onto the jet streak to remember where the better and worse snow will be. But, my memorization device for jet streaks will surely fall apart for me when my kids become better skiers than me.

the winds away from the lower pressure towards the higher pressure (usually southward). As air enters the jet streak, it accelerates. This increases the pressure gradient force, (i.e., the pressure gradient force vector pointing to the left (usually northwards) becomes longer than the Coriolis vector pointing to the right (usually southwards)). Thus, the air is being sent (i.e., converging) to the left entrance region, and as we learned in Chapter 2, this air is forced to descend creating downward pressure directly below. That is bad for snow. Simultaneously, the air is diverging in the right entrance region, as the pressure gradient force is overwhelming the Coriolis effect. This diverging air from the right entrance region, creates lift directly below it that creates snow. Once in the core of the jet streak, the air returns to its geostrophic balance – i.e., the pressure gradient force (pulling air to the left) and the Coriolis effect (pulling air to the right) balance each other out. But then as the air decelerates out of the exit region of the jet streak, the pressure gradient force weakens. As such, the opposite effects of the entrance region occur. The air converges to the right exit region where the Coriolis effect has not had time to adjust and decrease, but the left exit region has diverging air due to the weaker pressure gradient force. The diverging air at the left exit region creates lift below it that creates snow. Gosh this is complicated – it's just easier to memorize right entrance and left exit are good.

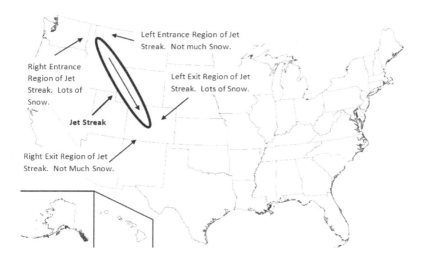

Left Entrance Region of Jet Streak. Not much Snow.

Right Entrance Region of Jet Streak. Lots of Snow.

Left Exit Region of Jet Streak. Lots of Snow.

Jet Streak

Right Exit Region of Jet Streak. Not Much Snow.

Practically, this means that when the jet streak approaches Colorado, if you're lucky enough to sit under the left exit region, it will dump snow like mad. It typically snows in intense bands of snow. Then, as the main portion of the jet streak passes overhead the weather may turn pleasant for a day or so, and if you are really lucky, the right entrance region will then pass over your area and it will dump snow again, again in intense bands of snow. I've certainly experienced this one-two punch before — it's awesome.

While weather models predict jet streak locations, the exact location and amount of snow caused by jet streaks is rather unpredictable. So, don't be surprised if forecasts based upon jet streaks either over-estimate or under-estimate the snowfall amounts significantly. By way of one example, in December 2019, the various weather models (which will be discussed in Chapters 10 and 11) were all predicting a powerful jet streak. I was putting together the weather forecast for my backcountry ski patrol looking at what each model forecasted. As the storm was starting up on a Thursday after-noon, of the four models I checked, one was calling for 2" of snow over the two-day storm, another 9", another 11", and the final one 19". That's quite a difference! Happily, the left exit region of the jet streak ended up directly over our backcountry patrol area, and we saw 16-20" of snow. But, had we not been so lucky, we could have seen only 2".

Predicting snow from jet streaks is a challenge. But it's probably easier than being a balloonist trying to catch a ride in a jet streak.

Chapter 6

Fronts and Convection: The Last Two Methods That Create Snow

Three down and two to go. Having addressed orographic lifting, low pressure, and jet streaks, the last fourth and fifth methods of snow production are the topic of this chapter. And okay, there is a sixth method, lake effect snow. However, as Colorado doesn't have lakes that are big enough to affect the weather, I'll relegate this topic to a footnote.[17] So, let's discuss the two final methods of snow production – fronts and convection – neither of which is important enough to warrant a chapter on its own.

---

[17] Okay, now that you're reading the boring footnote, let's talk about lake effect snow. Interestingly, unlike the other five methods of snow production, lake effect snow does not involve lifting per se. Lake effect snow is based upon the differing temperatures of the lake (warm) that is upwind, and the land (cold) that is downwind. The air above the lake and ground is impacted by these underlying temperatures. As winds blow across the lake, the air warms and picks up moisture from the lake as it passes over the lake. Once the now moist air passes the lake and is cooled by the colder land, it does what cooling moist air does. It snows. As Colorado does not have lakes large enough to have any real impact on snow, I think this quick description should be enough to keep you satisfied. My apologies to those readers who live and primarily ski in New York State. I'm sure you wish I wrote more on this topic.

FRONTS

In many ways the science of meteorology was born out of World War 1, so is it any surprise that the nascent field borrowed military terms to describe weather? The polar regions of the world create cold air masses. The tropical regions of the world create warm air masses, and the temperate regions (also called the mid-latitudes) are the battle ground between these air masses. Where does Colorado sit? Squarely in the battleground.

To be more technically accurate, the cold regions and the warm regions each produce two types of relevant air masses. Do you remember in Chapter One, how you as a cloud were born over the Pacific Ocean? Well, air masses originate from one of four (to keep it simple) types of regions. In Chapter One, you were born over cold water, so you were a cold-water air mass (what forecasters call maritime Polar). Had you been born further south in the Pacific Ocean, you would have been born over warm water, and so you would have been a warm water air mass (what forecasters call maritime Tropical). If you were born over land, you wouldn't have been a cloud because land is dry, and you would have been either born over cold land (what forecasters call continental Polar) or warm land (continental Tropical).

Contrary to what you may think, air does not like to mix. I experience this almost daily as my garage doesn't have air conditioning or heat like my house does. So, in the winter when I open the garage door, the air in the garage is relatively cold. But here's what is crazy. Even if I leave the door into my garage from my house open for a half an hour – the garage remains cold and my house remains warm. The cold garage air doesn't want to mix with the hot house air. Literally, these are mini airmasses, which like to stay separate. The front between them is at my mud room between the house and the garage. And air masses hate mixing even more when they're large, like the air masses we're discussing in this chapter.

Cold airmasses typically come from the northwest. If a cold airmass hits a warmer air mass (whether wet or dry) sitting over Colorado, the cold air drives under the warmer air. This is easy to remember, as warm air tends to rise. (This is why it's called a hot-air balloon and not a cold-air balloon.) The denser cold airmass pushing under the warm airmass creates a steep boundary between the warm air and the cold air. The warm airmass is being pushed up by the cold air mass. And when I say a steep boundary, the point is that the warm air is being forced upward quickly and in a short distance, as opposed to gradually over a longer distance.

Now, what did we learn in Chapter 1 about what happens when air is lifted? Imagine you are the cloud in the warm airmass. The cold airmass pushes under, which lifts you up. As you gain in elevation, you cool down. This means that the temperature decreases enough to first form clouds and then form precipitation (hopefully snow as opposed to rain). As the cold air mass attacks the warm air mass at a steep angle, cold fronts typically produce intense snow for 4 to 6 hours. As the cold air mass is the one invading, so to speak, this is called a **cold front**.

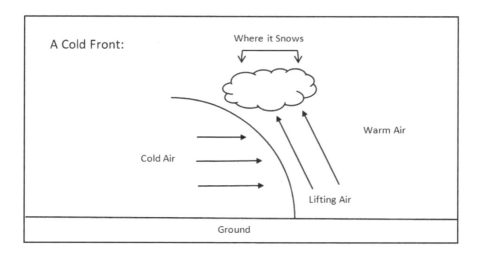

If a warm air mass invades, typically from the southwest, and pushes out a colder air mass, this is called a **warm front**. Again, it makes sense that warm fronts come from the southwest as the south produces the warmth and winds tend to blow from west to east. As the warm air mass collides with the cold airmass, the warm airmass begins climbing over the denser cold air mass, again because warm air rises. As the warm air mass rises over the cold air mass, the warm air expands which causes it to cool down (remember that term adiabatic cooling)? Air cools as it gains elevation, that causes clouds and then precipitation.

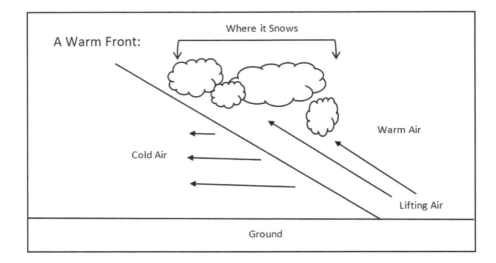

As the angle that the warm air rises over the cold air is much shallower, the snow produced from a warm front tends to be much more slow and steady than from a cold front. A warm front typically produces roughly 12 to 18 hours of snowfall.

As the attack angle of a cold front is much steeper than a warm front, the cold front violently pushes air upwards in elevation. This produces snowfall for a much shorter time period (roughly 4 to 6 hours), but the snowfall is far more intense during this time than during the passage of a warm front.

On weather surface maps (think the big weather map in the USA Today), warm fronts are shown in red with semi-circles facing the direction it is advancing. Cold fronts are shown in blue with triangles facing the direction it is advancing.[18] Unless you generally ski on the east side of the continental

---

[18] Technically, there are two other types of fronts. Stationary fronts are ones in which neither airmass is advancing, and they are shown in alternating red and blue. They produce little moisture. An occluded front is where an advancing cold front (which tend to move faster than warm fronts) overtakes an advancing warm front. This is shown in purple. Although an occluded front produces precipitation, it is generally short lived. These types of fronts are unimportant enough to be relegated to a footnote.

divide, don't waste too much brain power on understanding fronts. Much like low pressure circulation, fronts tend to break down over the Colorado mountains.

CONVECTION

For the sake of completeness, there's one other method that drives water vapor higher into the sky, causing it to cool and come down (occasionally) as snow in Colorado. And that's *convection*.

Convection is what causes thunderstorms. The ground tends to be warmer than the air. We'll hit this point again when discussing recycled powder and yet again when discussing avalanche science. When air is heated over land (because land tends to be warm), it rises. That rising forces it to cool, which in turn can create precipitation. This normally is a late spring and summer phenomenon producing thunderstorms and rain. However, this does occur occasionally in the winter, or more often in the springtime, producing snow. When this occurs, often there may be heavy snow. It is pretty hard to predict exactly where convection will occur. It's even more challenging than predicting where jet streaks will create snow. Think of summertime thunderstorms, how it will rain like hell in one location, and only a few miles away there'll be no rain. When you translate this to the wintertime, the (perhaps humorous) forecast of a trace to 20 inches of snowfall may be about as accurate as one can get with convection fueled snow.

Now that you are armed with a more general understanding of the multiple snow producing weather patterns, let's switch gears and discuss how snow itself is formed.

PART 2

THE MICRO AND MACRO OF SNOW AND WEATHER

Now that we've discussed what causes snow, it's time to dive into what exactly is snow, and why it forms. On the size scale, we're talking about microscopic issues. And it's helpful to know these microscopic issues. It's also important to understand the macroscopic issues – how global weather impacts whether tomorrow will be a powder day, a sunny day, or both. And, once we've talked about the very small and the very large, I figured let's try to put together the concepts of the last two chapters into one whopper of an example – the great March 2003 blizzard.

Chapter 7

How a Snowflake is Born: Explaining Snow Crystal Formation

So, what exactly is snow? We've talked about what causes snow – moist air rising in elevation – but that doesn't answer the question of what causes snow crystals, the building blocks of the snowflake.

Let's get some terminology out of the way at the outset. And don't worry, the first two terms are pretty simple though a surprising number of people don't know the difference.

A *snow crystal* is a crystal of ice. They are six-sided ice crystals. And, the ice crystals with long branches, feature in every cartoon about snow and are seemingly printed on every Christmas Card.

As snow crystals fall from the cloud, they clump together as *snowflakes*. So, a snowflake is simply a bunch of snow crystals stuck together.

Before we dive into the details of snow crystal formation, let's start with a bit of trivia. The cartoons and Christmas Cards of snow crystals show them in the wrong color. Contrary to popular belief, snow crystals are not white. I can hear you yelling – what! Did the author just say snow isn't white?!?!

Well, snow appears white, but snow crystals are not actually white themselves. Hang on, let me explain. The next time you catch a snowflake as it falls, take a close look at the edges of each individual snow crystal in the snowflake. Each one is clear. And they're clear because ice is clear. If you look at salt or sugar under a microscope, you'll see that they are clear too. Light scatters off the almost countless tiny surfaces of the snow crystals (or salt crystals or sugar crystals), and the sum of these reflections appear to be white.

Let's use an every-day example. Rain is colorless and clear – the only reason why clouds appear white is because that's the way light reflects off the countless water droplets that make up the cloud. Similarly, ground up glass appears white. So, next time you look at a slope covered in freshly fallen snow, don't forget, even though it looks white, it's made up of tiny ice crystals that are colorless and transparent.

Anyhow, I digress. Back to snow crystal formation.

Any discussion of snow crystal formation should start with a caveat. The details of snow crystal formation are still not well understood. After all, snow crystal formation occurs on the microscopic level thousands of feet above us, which is not the easiest thing to study. If you do invent a device that can analyze microscopically small droplets thousands of feet in the air that are moving rapidly, please let me know. I want in on that patent. While mankind has made great strides in studying snow crystal formation, mostly in the refrigerated laboratory setting, there is still a long way to go. Like most scientific endeavors, our great grandchildren will likely admire what we got right with our limited technology and laugh about what we got so wrong. With that caveat out of the way, let's discuss how a snow crystal is formed.

As you know already, the air always contains water vapor. And, the air also contains countless specks of microscopic dust, salt, bacteria, soil, etc. As it's easier just to think of all of these as specks of dust, we'll just call it dust for the rest of the chapter. How microscopic is this dust? You could line up a million of these specks end-to-end, and they would be just a millimeter long. In other words, a million of them would add up to only the size of a single coffee ground.

When water vapor in the air is sufficiently cooled (usually by being pushed upward in elevation), tiny water droplets form around the microscopic dust. The dust that each tiny water droplet condenses onto are called **condensation nuclei**. These droplets are now far bigger than the dust specks (that is, the condensation nuclei), but they are still tiny. You'd have to line 50,000 of them end to end to be just one millimeter long.

At the same time as the water droplets are forming, tiny ice crystals are simultaneously forming. In fact, they can actually start forming before the tiny water droplets begin forming. The ice crystals freeze around only certain types of dust with the proper chemical structure. These particular type of dust on which ice crystals form are called *freezing nuclei*. The colder the cloud is, the easier it is for the ice crystal to form. Below minus forty degrees (either Fahrenheit or Celsius as minus forty is the same temperature under either scale), the ice will freeze spontaneously without the help of the freezing nuclei.[19] Regardless, although snow can be produced by a cloud just

---

[19] While I try to provide Celsius numbers in this chapter to accompany Fahrenheit numbers, at the risk of being controversial, let me just say it. Fahrenheit is a way better scale than Celsius when it comes to weather. It's so much more descriptive and practical that a cold winter day is 0 degrees and a hot summer day is 100 degrees. Saying a cold winter day is -17 degrees Celsius, and a hot summer day is 38 degrees Celsius is a dumb range. Message to the rest of the world: you can keep your Celsius scale. I like my Fahrenheit scale. It's far more practical for the range of weather we live in. If all I did with my entire life was to boil and freeze water over and over and over again, then I suppose Celsius would be better. But for actual living, Fahrenheit is the better scale.

And while I'm on my rant, I can generally pass on the metric system. You may have learned in grade school math that people like the base ten system, which is why the metric system is so superior to the English system of measurements. But stop and think about that for a minute. The only reason we like base ten is because we have ten fingers. Math (and the metric system) would be far better if we had twelve fingers. Try to divide a meter into thirds. How do you find 33.33333333333333 centimeters on a ruler? Pretty quickly it makes sense why carpenters prefer the foot to the meter.

And, while the rational metric measurement system is supposedly based on base ten, much of the other universal measurements are not in base 10. And, they're not in base 12, i.e., 12 inches in a foot, either. The Europeans, like us Americans, have some pretty weird numbers for measurements. We have 60 minutes in an hour (a base 60 system), 24 hours in a day (a base 24 system), seven days in a week (a base 7 system), and roughly 52 weeks in a year (a base 52 system). How absurdly complicated is that? Ironically, during the French Revolution, France attempted to change these measurements to base 10. There were ten hours in a day, ten days in a week, etc. Did people like the simplicity?

below freezing, most freezing only occurs below 21 degrees Fahrenheit (-6 Celsius). This raises the interesting point that it is a popular misconception that the freezing point of water in any liquid form is 32 degrees Fahrenheit (0 degrees Celsius). This isn't exactly correct. 32 degrees Fahrenheit is the freezing temperature for impure water – that is, water with the freezing nuclei. Water can exist in its liquid phase well below 32 degrees – and the term for this very cold water is appropriately called **supercooled**.

Anyhow, there are both ice crystals and supercooled water droplets floating around in the cloud. At a microscopic level, which we're still at, the vapor pressure is higher in the water droplets than in the ice crystals. Just like winds move from high pressure to low pressure, the water in the droplets convert to the gaseous phase, moving from the water droplets to the ice crystals, and depositing the vapor on the ice crystals. Voila, you have a **snow crystal**! Under the right conditions, these deposits grow out in long branches, which create the beautiful and best quality snow crystals, **stellar dendrites**. Perhaps it is only by chance that the most beautiful snow crystals, which grace our Christmas Cards and silly looking sweaters, also happen to be the best ones for powder snow.

It is hardly surprising from this discussion that the two key components in determining the type of snow crystals that grow in a cloud are temperature and humidity. But, the type of snow crystal grown based upon those combinations of temperature and humidity are surprising. These crystals are best shown in a crystal morphology diagram.

No, they hated it. Napoleon did away with the system within a year after becoming emperor.

So stop telling me that the metric units are better than the English units. They're not. I'll give you that there are exceptions. For example, millibars of pressure. This metric system is great as sea level averages 1000 millibars of pressure and half the atmosphere averages 500 millibars of pressure. Otherwise, I'll stick with my freedom units, thank you very much.

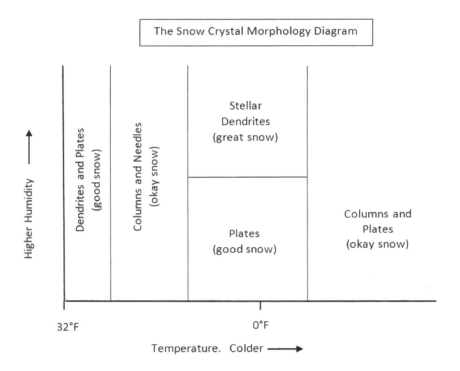

The Snow Crystal Morphology Diagram

All snow is good. But, it seems as if there's a Goldilocks temperature for the best snow crystal formation. At the right temperature, long dendritic arms grow on the crystals. The best snow for skiing is formed between roughly 15 degrees and -5 degrees Fahrenheit (-10 to -22 Celsius), when the cloud is supersaturated. (To confuse things, great dendrite ice crystals also grow around the comparatively warm 28 degrees, but let's not confuse ourselves too much with this minor point.) Decent snow is produced above 15 degrees and below 0 degrees, but it's not as great as the snow in that Goldilocks zone. And, below about -20 degrees, it starts to get too cold for decent snow production.

This information may explain, at least in part, why Colorado gets such good powder. With high elevations and cold nights – we're in the right spot on the temperature axis for great powder when our clouds lift and get supersaturated.

Remember in Chapter 2, I discussed how Colorado snow is lighter be-cause it's far from any ocean. This is true not because the clouds are more dry, so to speak. Supersaturation is required to produce snow – whether a foot from the ocean or a thousand miles from the ocean. Rather, land doesn't hold heat as well as water. The sun beats down the most on the summer solstice – June 21st – and the top temperatures in Colorado follow just a touch over a month later. Land holds heat, but it doesn't hold heat anything like the ocean. Have you ever wondered why hurricanes occur in the fall? It's because the water continues to heat way past the summer solstice, so the ocean is at its warmest in the early fall. As warm ocean temperatures are the fuel for hurricanes, hurricanes are a fall phenomenon. During the winter, areas far from the warmer ocean cool down much quicker and stay colder. And, the lack of a nearby ocean permits a greater day-night temperature fluctuation. So, while Colorado typically has warm winter days, it has bitterly cold nights. It's far colder in Colorado than in places closer to the ocean. And what does that mean? Our clouds are usually in the powder growing mood – with temperatures in that snow crystal formation Goldilocks zone. So, while Colorado tends to see the best light snow – the true cause is the nighttime temperature because we're so far from the ocean (and so high), not the lack of nighttime humidity.[20]

What's the lesson out of this for predicting powder? As the greatest snow, the stellar dendrites, are produced best at cloud temperatures between roughly 15 degrees and -5 degrees Fahrenheit (-10 to -22 Celsius), the best storms for snow tend to be in this temperature range. Fortunately, orographic lifting means that the snow producing clouds are not much higher than the top of the mountains on which they are dumping. So, as a rule of thumb, if you take the top of the mountain and subtract 5-10 degrees Fahrenheit, you can get a good guess whether you're in the Goldilocks zone for stellar dendrite production or not.[21] If you are, don't be surprised if you get more snow than forecasted.

---

[20]   Also, near the ocean, when it is warmer the water droplets freeze onto the falling ice crystals, which creates a denser snow (in a process called riming or accretion). This almost never happens in Colorado.

[21]   If the snow is being created by an upper atmosphere phenomenon (like Jet Streaks discussed in Chapter 5) as opposed to orographic lifting, the snow

For a good size snow crystal to grow, it takes between fifteen minutes to an hour. As the snow crystal grows, it becomes heavier and eventually starts to fall. As it falls through the cloud, it continues to grow until it falls below the cloud where there are no longer the water droplets to feed it. At this point, without wind, it falls at roughly one mile an hour towards our favorite ski spots.

But it gets more complex. A cloud isn't a single solid mass at the same temperature and humidity. So different types of snow crystals are being created in different parts of the cloud at the same time. And to make it even more complicated, a snow crystal doesn't just grow in one part of the cloud, but it gets bounced around as it grows – one of the many reasons why no two snowflakes are ever alike – so generalizations about temperature and humidity must remain generalizations.

I hope you have enjoyed this brief tour through snow crystal formation and growth. But I hope it hasn't distracted you from the more critical questions of what causes water vapor in the atmosphere to rise. That question, addressed in Chapters 2-6, is the more important concept in understanding where to find powder. Just remember that mountain-top temperatures in the 0 degree to 20 degree range can often produce the lightest snow in the clouds above them.

At this point you may be asking yourself why there might be a week of nothing but snow in Colorado, and then a week of nothing but sun. Let's turn to that question in our next chapter.

---

crystals will form much higher in the atmosphere. As such, the temperatures higher aloft matter more than the temperatures just above the mountain tops.

Chapter 8

Good and Bad Weather: The Story of Troughs and Ridges

W hen my son was three, he commented out-of-the-blue, as three-year-old kids often do, "Daddy, you hate bridges." I looked at him puzzled. I asked him, "what do you mean?" He simply repeated, "you hate bridges." I looked at him and said: "there's nothing wrong with bridges. We need them to get over streams and rivers." He fought back. "No daddy! You hate bridges. They stop snow." I was about to ask him how that was possible when it dawned on me what he was saying.

"Do you mean ridges," I asked? "Yes, bridges" he responded. "Well," I said, "I do hate ridges."

While they are ridges, not bridges, my son is absolutely right. I hate blocking ridges. So, what is a blocking ridge? Let's start by changing the scale. In the last chapter on the birth of a snowflake, the science was mostly microscopic. When it comes to troughs and ridges, you have to think of the whole planet.

I already introduced the concept of the jet stream in Chapter 5, in order to explain the snow producing jet streaks. We're going to return to the concept of the jet stream in this chapter, to explain what are ridges and troughs, and why people who hunt powder care about them.

As a reminder, air near the equator is warm and air near the poles is cold. Air masses with different temperatures have different pressures. And pressure differences drive winds.

As such, the jet stream forms in the upper atmosphere as a current of air that separates the warmer and colder air masses. As temperature differences vary (i.e., it's not always 30 degrees warmer in Dallas than in Detroit), the jet stream is never in a fixed location. Similarly, large geographic features on the surface – like our wonderful Rocky Mountains – impact the flow of the jet stream. So, the location and strength of the jet stream is always changing.

As an aside, when I say the jet stream is in the upper atmosphere, what do I mean? You are always under an ocean of air; the majority of that air extends from the top of your head to the top of the **troposphere**. If you've ever seen the anvil shape at the top of a thunderhead – i.e., where a really tall thunderhead flattens out at a very high height, that is the top of the troposphere. Above the troposphere is the ozone layer that marks the lower portion of the **stratosphere**, the next level up in the earth's atmosphere.[22]

Basically, all weather occurs in the troposphere. And the vast majority of the earth's air is in the troposphere. The exact height of the troposphere varies significantly based upon latitude (lower above the poles and higher above the equator) and time of the year, but just to give you a rough sense, it averages roughly seven and a half miles high or 40,000 feet. That means it is six and a half miles above Denver, and five miles above most of Colorado's ski areas. Put another way, the length of Vail's back bowls from end to end is greater than the distance from those back bowls to the top of the troposphere. When my son asks me how high the sky is, I can respond with a straight face, "not very high."

The jet stream tends to be just below the top of the troposphere. In meteorology speak, it's at the 300 and 250 millibar level, which will be explained in Chapter 14. Briefly, millibars measure air pressure. Conveniently, 1000 millibars is the approximate air pressure at sea level. So, if you ascend in a balloon from sea level (roughly 1000 millibars) to the jet stream (roughly 300 millibars in the winter), there will be 30% of the air present at that elevation as there is at sea level. And if you are crazy enough to try to ride the jet stream in a balloon, you don't have to worry about hitting mountains. If

---

[22]   Things get weird when discussing the stratosphere. In the stratosphere, adiabatic cooling no longer works – the lapse rate goes from positive to negative. In other words, the higher one goes in the stratosphere, the warmer it gets.

you are in the jet stream, you're already above (albeit just a hair above) the summit of Mt. Everest.

As I mentioned, the jet stream also isn't just a straight-line following lines of latitude around the earth. Rather, temperature differences in conjunction with physical barriers such as our own mighty Rocky Mountains (as well as other global features) cause the jet stream to move in a wave pattern. While the Rocky Mountains are well below the height of the jet stream, their effect on air patterns extends up to the jet stream. And they help to create the waves.

Conveniently, the larger waves are called long waves and the smaller waves are called short waves.[23] The short waves are basically ripples in a long wave. And while the fact that the jet stream isn't straight makes weather forecasting much more complicated, it's a good thing as it creates colder and snowier weather over Colorado.

There are usually between three to seven long waves as the jet stream circumnavigates the upper atmosphere. Their location is always changing. However, their location changes slowly compared to many other meteorological phenomena – which means that they can influence weather in one location for a while. If you were somehow able to take a snapshot from outer space above the north pole showing just the polar air mass, it would look like a giant three to seven leaf clover (without a stem of course) placed on top of the earth. The edges of the three (or more) leaf clover would be the jet stream and the bulges of the leaves would be the long waves.

These waves create the more long-term weather patterns during the winter. The impact of a wave may last for only a day or two, but they can also last for a week or two. When the jet stream stays to the north of Colorado, even if it dips south in other parts of the country, we have a **ridge**. This means there will be warm air and high pressure in Colorado. Ridges are bad. I hate them. They mean sun, warm temperatures, and not much snow. But they do provide lots of vitamin D and silly goggle tan lines.

---

[23]   Confusingly, these are also called planetary waves and/or Rossby waves.

The opposite of a ridge is a *trough*. A trough is simply an elongated area of low pressure. When the upper-level winds dip down over Colorado (by analogy we're now placed under the three to seven leaf clover), we have a long wave trough of cold air and low pressure air. Low pressure is good as it causes lift, which causes snow. And cold air is good as it helps with snow. So, troughs are good.

If you're curious, these features are called ridges and troughs, because that's exactly what they are – just vertically higher or lower locations of air. Recall from Chapter 4 that as the air at the equator is hot from direct overhead sunlight, it expands? This means that at the equator, the top height of the troposphere is higher in elevation than average. The poles are cold, on the other hand, and as cold air is denser, the top elevation of the troposphere is lower in elevation at the poles. As cold air from closer to the poles invades southwards to Colorado (that is the trough), literally the height of the air at the same air pressure level is lower. And, as warm air from closer to the equator invades northwards to Colorado (that is the ridge), the height of the air at the same air pressure level is higher. Thus, the terms trough and ridge are exactly what they are – masses of air that are shorter (trough) and taller (ridge) in elevation.

If you're still confused on this point (don't worry if you are, this is a tricky concept), let me take a step back to the balloonist analogy in Chapter 5. If you're reading this book, I'm sure you prefer to ski than to golf. But, I'm sure you have friends who are not as wise as you, and who prefer to golf than ski. Imagine one of your golfing friends heads to southern Arizona to go golfing in February while at the same time you head to Montana to go skiing. Setting aside the fact that you are having more fun than your friend because you are skiing, let's say each of you decide to take a break halfway through your trip for an afternoon of ballooning. (I know this sounds silly – but this is an educational tool, not a real-life example!) You go up in your balloon in Montana, while your golfer friend goes up in his or her balloon in Arizona. You both carry pressure gauges (also known as barometers) on your respective balloons, and you both agree to stop your balloon from rising once you reach 50% of air pressure, i.e., the 500 millibar level. When you are both at the elevation of 50% air pressure, i.e., 500 millibars, will:

[a] you be at a higher elevation than your golfer friend;

[b] you be at the same elevation as your golfer friend; or

[c] you be at a lower elevation than your golfer friend?

Remember, warm air is less dense than cold air. Warm air expands. So, the warmer air in Arizona goes higher into the atmosphere. So, your golfer friend's balloon will be at a higher elevation at the same air pressure than you will be. The correct answer is [c].

Describing this another way, the 500 millibar level (that's the air pressure level that both of you stopped your balloons) is higher in Arizona than in Montana. After all, your golfer friend's balloon is higher than your balloon at the same pressure level. Compared to your balloon, your friend is riding on a ridge of high pressure. And you, in your balloon above Montana, is much lower – you are in a trough.

When conditions are sunny and pleasant in Colorado – which sucks – it's often due to a ridge of high pressure invading Colorado from the south. If conditions are cold and wet – which is awesome – it's often due to a trough of low pressure invading Colorado from the north. And, the zone between the troughs and ridges is where the jet stream and jet streaks occur. As you learned in Chapter 5, the jet stream moves in a wave pattern, as do the troughs to the north and the ridges to the south of the jet stream.

So, if you were to now take a balloon from Colorado straight up in the atmosphere to the 50% air pressure level, that is, 500 millibars, and somehow anchor it to keep it from moving laterally, over the next few weeks you could tell by your elevation what would be going on with the weather. As your balloon ascends in elevation to stay at the 50th percentile line of air, a ridge of high pressure is approaching Colorado. And as a skier, that's a horrible time. On the other hand, when you're descending in elevation, a trough of low pressure is coming, which is usually a good sign for skiing.

If one makes a map showing the elevation of a certain elevation of air pressure – it's very much like a topographical map.

So, we know being in a trough is good. Where is the best place to be within a trough? Typically, the best location for the wave to be is for it to be heading back northward just to our west. (Picture the wave heading southward over Nevada and curving over southern Utah and coming back north over far western Colorado.) This spins out the most moisture and storms into Colorado. The reason why is complicated, but think of the air stream in the trough as a road with lots of traffic. As the road dips southward it narrows – like going from four lanes to two lanes on a highway. This slows traffic so to speak. The air slows creating greater density and thus raises the high pressure directly below. As the air moves through the curve and starts heading back north, the air current widens – the equivalent of the highway going from two lanes to four lanes letting all the cars speed up. With faster moving air, the density decreases creating low pressure directly below it. And, as you learned in Chapter 4, low pressure is good.

With this understanding of long waves, short waves, ridges, and troughs, let me throw out a few more related terms.

If you ever read the word *vorticity* in a forecast discussion, don't get worried by this complicated sounding term, and its related terms. Vorticity is simply the measure of the spin of a system.[24] There is often significant vorticity near the southern end of the long or short wave as described in more depth in the footnote.

When ridges and troughs are nearly stationary owing to the location of the upper-level winds, they are often referred to as **blocks**, such as a blocking ridge. A ridge (remember, that's the bad one where the warmer air is winning) blocks snowy weather from approaching Colorado. And that is truly bad. No wonder my son thinks I hate bridges so much.

But just as these nearly stationary ridges can be bad, the relatively stationary nature of these patterns also means the opposite is true. Troughs can keep Colorado snowy for days or weeks at a time.

And then, there is the arguably greatest of all weather patterns, the **cut-off low**.

Picture the bottom of the wave (i.e., south / southeast edge) of the jet stream, forming a trough that runs just to the north end of Colorado. As the jet stream moves back northeast, the furthest south area of snowier colder air can get squeezed off from the rest of the jet stream. It is now cut-off from the colder air, without the upper-level winds to drive it more quickly from west to east across the country. Now what? Being cut-off from the main flow, it hangs out and meanders in whatever direction it pleases, while dumping copious quantities of snow beneath it.

---

[24] There are some terms related to vorticity that you may hear in a forecast discussion – but don't worry, in spite of their names, they're not nearly as complicated as they sound. Vorticity measures spin, and the spin component is usually greatest at the bottom of the wave – as it typically curves from heading towards the southeast to heading towards the northeast. This is the vorticity maximum (or vort max). And, following the wave back northward is the location of positive vorticity advection (or PVA), which creates the low pressure below it. Positive vorticity advection is a good thing. Forecasters look for it as it means stronger low pressures, which means snow. (See Chapter 4.)

As an aside, advection is just a fancy word for movement. So, if a forecast says: "Ahead of this feature, there will be considerable moisture *advecting* into the region," that just means that ahead of the feature there will be considerable moisture *heading* into the region.

Cut-off lows are unpredictable because it's nearly impossible to predict their path as they meander. They are literally "cut-off" from the main airflow, which is far more predictable. And these wonderful meandering monsters can produce massive snowstorms as they stall and snow.

Chapter 9

Putting It All Together: The March 2003 Blizzard

So, let's put the information from all the previous chapters together, using the greatest snowstorm within recent memory in the Front Range of Colorado – the legendary March 2003 blizzard – as an example.

At the time I lived in downtown Denver, two blocks from the office I worked at. The storm started in earnest on Tuesday, was at its zenith on Wednesday, and continued to pummel Denver all day on Thursday. On the Wednesday of the storm, I trudged through the deep snow to the office. Certain that all restaurants would be closed that day, as it approached lunch time, I decided to walk the office halls and invite anyone actually in the office to my apartment for lunch. There was no one to invite. It turns out that of the over 100 employees at the firm, I was the only one who made it into the office that day. There was just too much snow for anyone who wasn't walking to make it into downtown Denver.

That Saturday, wanting to wait until the avalanche danger subsided a bit more, but with the roads reopened, I went with my friends to A-Basin (the closest ski area to Denver to which I had a season pass that year). And, we were underwhelmed. They got a decent amount of snow, but nothing like what we were expecting. On Sunday we went to backcountry ski at Berthoud Pass, and the skiing was off-the-charts.

By this point in the book, you probably have a good sense of what happened in this legendary blizzard.

As you just learned in Chapter 8, when a low pressure system gets cutoff from the predominant upper atmosphere winds, it can remain stationary or just meander slightly about for several days. This is the cutoff low. And as you learned in Chapter 4, low pressures cause air to rise. Rising air means cooling air, which means snow. And this is exactly what occurred in March 2003 when the closed low pressure was cut-off and simply sat to the southeast of Denver for days producing an epic snowstorm.

And what happened? As the cut-off low wasn't moving, Denver got almost three feet of snow. That's amazing!

But what is more amazing is what happens when you combine the cutoff low with what we learned in Chapters 2 and 3, about orographic lifting. The winds blowing from the east towards the west were pushing the moisture up the east side of Colorado's front range mountains. This is an upslope storm, caused by a cut-off low. The mountains forcing the clouds to rise produced even more snow than just the low pressure doing the work on its own.

Eldora Mountain was unsurprisingly the biggest ski area winner of the storm. Why? Eldora is in a prime location to catch upslope snow as it is in the area in which the air is still being lifted as it approaches the Continental Divide from the east. Eldora saw six and a half feet of snow. (Thank you orographic lifting from east to west).[25]

A few backcountry spots east of the divide topped out with just over seven feet of snow. Loveland (straddling the continental divide) and Winter Park (just west of the continental divide) saw almost six feet of snow. Copper Mountain, however, sitting further west of the continental divide, only saw two feet of snow — less than Denver. And Vail got only a foot. This is classic orographic lifting, spillover, and precipitation shadow — just with the winds blowing from the east and joyfully measured in feet of snow as opposed to inches of snow.

Armed with this basic understanding, it's easy to look at weather forecasts and get a sense based upon wind direction, jet stream location, and moisture whether it'll snow or be dry. And that is the topic of the next part of our book — weather forecasting.

---

[25] Echo Mountain wasn't open in 2003. Like Eldora, it would have seen a tremendous amount of snow if it was open.

PART 3

PREDICTING THE FUTURE (ROUND ONE): UNDERSTANDING WEATHER MODELS

Trying to predict the future has always been one of mankind's greatest challenges. As Yogi Berra once said, "it's tough to make predictions, especially about the future."

There are a few professions that do an amazingly good job predicting the future. For example, physicists tend to be incredible at this crazy task. Think about any Mars rover mission. Physicists not only have to perfectly predict where Mars will be in its revolution around the sun half a year to a year from when the rocket ship (with the rover in it) is launched from the Earth. Physicists also must perfectly predict where in Mars' rotation around its own axis at that precise time the rocket ship will show up many months from now, not to mention predict where is Earth in its revolution and rotation when takeoff occurs. To successfully land a rover on Mars takes an amazing ability to predict the future.

Let's take a look at the opposite end of the spectrum. You know who is really bad at predicting the future? Every talking head in the world who discusses short-term financial investments. If any single one of them could accurately predict the S&P 500 a mere day into the future, let alone a week into the future, they would be billionaires within a month. Money managers and financial speculators are, without doubt, the worst futurists. The groundhog on Groundhog's Day, Punxsutawney Phil, has them beat by a mile.

Where do meteorologists fall? If you compare them to physicists, they are a joke. A physicist can predict the precise time and location of a solar eclipse a century in the future. No forecaster can predict the precise time and location of a snowfall two days in the future. But if you compare weather forecasters to the alleged financial gurus, weather forecasters are the greatest prognosticators that ever lived.[26]

So, what does it take to predict the weather? And why are forecasts usually right when it comes to the big picture in the short term, and often completely useless when it comes either to precise details or in truly long-range forecasts?

In order to understand a weather forecast, you have to first understand how it is created. Most of weather forecasting is based upon weather forecast models. Without them, there would be no weather forecasts that are even slightly reliable beyond perhaps a day. So, if you care about powder, you should care about the weather models.

In this part of the book, let's examine what are weather models, how they work, and what you can and cannot learn from them.

---

[26]   7News Meteorologist Mike Nelson, in his great book, *Colorado Weather Almanac*, jokes that people shouldn't give him and his fellow meteorologists a hard time. After all, he's the only person on the local news who predicts the future. His fellow newscasters aren't getting on television to predict what will happen over the next week – they just report on the past.

Chapter 10

The Three Major Global Forecast Models

In Reading England sit two supercomputers. Each supercomputer conducts tens of trillions of calculations every second, pulling data from land, sea, sky, and satellite in order to produce a weather forecast for the entire globe. How does it do this? Weather is just a very complicated physics problem – or should I say many many many complicated physics problems. With its tremendous computing power for our time, the model takes the current weather conditions and applies the laws of thermodynamics, hydrodynamics, the sphericity of the earth, the rotation of the earth, the composition of the atmosphere, the topography of the land, the location of the oceans, the ocean currents, ... well, I could keep going, but you get the point ... to calculate a forecast for every part of the globe for the next 15 days.

This forecast produced by these supercomputers in Reading England is commonly called *the European Model*. The European Model is technically named: the IFS (Integrated Forecast System) of the ECMWF (European Centre for Medium-Range Weather Forecasts). Due to the alphabet soup of its actual name, you can see why it's easier for us Americans to just call it the European Model. And, the European Model is arguably the gold standard when it comes to weather forecasting.

Depending upon the study, the European Model is considered to be reliably skillful (in other words, better than just relying upon historical average weather data) at least six days into the future. In practice, it often accurately predicts storms much further out than six days. Now and again, it gets a prediction generally right out ten days or more. Of course, I'm reminded of the old joke — *don't give meteorologists a hard time, they accurately predicted twelve of the last five snowstorms.*

Not impressed with the European Model's six-day reliably skillful forecasting ability? You should be. Since first being created in the 1970s, every decade or so the European Model is able to gain an additional day of forecasting predictions that are consistently more accurate than the baseline. In the 1990s, the European Model was only reliably skillful four days into the future.

And think about how tough it is to create a multi-day forecast. As addressed above, the model looks at current conditions and runs a series of physics equations based upon the myriad of current conditions to forecast how the weather will change one day from now. If the model wants to forecast two days out, it will take the one day out forecast, treat that as the current conditions, and run the calculations based upon the forecasted conditions to forecast the following day. (This is oversimplified, but accurate enough for the point I'm making.) So, what is a six-day forecast? It's a forecast, based upon a forecast, based upon a forecast, based upon a forecast, based upon a forecast, based upon a forecast, based upon today's weather. The fact that at this point it's consistently more reliable than historical averages is pretty impressive.

Still not impressed with its six-day reliably skillful forecast ability? Well, tough. The European Model is arguably the best all-around weather model we humans have so far developed. But the European Model is not without faults. It only runs twice a day. It is still somewhat weak at predicting the intricacies of snowfall in mountainous terrain. And most importantly, the [expletive deleted] Europeans, unlike most of the rest of the world, charge through the nose to access their model. While there is a website I use that provides the European Model information for free, it doesn't have nearly the wealth of information that the cooler countries provide from their free models.

The American equivalent of the European Model is **the American (GFS) Model** (that is, the Global Forecast System Model). While the American Model maybe not held in quite as high esteem as the European Model, take solace fellow Americans, unlike the European Model, the GFS Model is free and publicly available.[27] Choose the GFS link at this website: https://mag.ncep.noaa.gov/model-guidance-model-area.php to access the model. It provides dozens of hour-by-hour predictions (temperatures, winds, precipitation, relative humidity, etc.) at multiple levels of the atmosphere.

And, if you find that website unwieldy on your cell phone, there are many other choices for accessing the same model in a more simplified version. If I'm looking to pull the data intensive GFS Model up on my phone when I have sketchy cell reception, I use the much less data intensive summary, courtesy of George Mason University, found at http://wxmaps.org/fcst.php. This provides daily predictions of some key items.

As the GFS Model is free, and it provides so much information in an easy-to-use format, it is the first model I myself look at for trying to get a sense of weather at a continent-wide scale and in the medium range (i.e., 4-10 days). Thank you Uncle Sam!

The Canadian Model (technically, the GDPS or Global Deterministic Prediction System portion of the Global Environmental Multiscale Model) is also a global weather model, frequently used for mountain forecasting. It's usually not regarded quite as highly for all-around weather forecasting as either the European Model or the American Model, but it's probably a close third in the race for all-around medium range weather forecasting. It's definitely a step ahead for mountain forecasting of the handful of other global forecast models that I don't address in the book. Three global models, after all, is enough to fill one's head. And for what it's worth, the Canadian Model is often my favorite of the three global models when it comes to snowfall. (See Appendix G.)

And, Canada is as cool (no pun intended) as the United States. The Canadians provide free access around the world to their models. Here is the link: https://weather.gc.ca/model_forecast/global_e.html.

---

[27]   Indeed, the silver medal when it comes to numerical weather prediction models probably goes to *the UKMET Model* (that is, the model operated by the United Kingdom METeorological Agency). I'd write more about this model, but as people tend to like groups of three as opposed to groups of four, we'll ignore this model for now.

Chapter 11

The Three Major Regional Forecast Models and Comparing Models

A t this point, I've now introduced three of the six forecast models worth discussing. These three models are the triumvirate of medium-term weather models. The European Model, the American (GFS) Model, and the Canadian (GDPS) Model all share the same basic attributes, they are all global models predicting weather over the entire earth both in the short and medium range. And this takes extraordinary computing power.

On shorter time-horizons (think out 2-4 days), and smaller scale (think North America), computer models can run more calculations that can hopefully be more accurate than the global medium-term forecasts. So, if you want a more detailed model of what should occur closer to now, it's time to turn our attention to the regional models. Like the triumvirate of medium-term global models, for the purposes of forecasting Colorado snow, there is a triumvirate of regional short-term models. They are the NAM, the RDPS, and the WRF.

My apologies for the alphabet soup, and trust me, I'm skipping over many other models to keep this simple. The NAM is the American government model, the GDPS is the Canadian government model, and I like to think of the WRF as the university model, as it was NCAR, the consortium of universities, that created it. So, let's go through each of these three short-term regional models.

The NAM Model, or North American Model, is a product of the United States Government. Like the American (GFS) Model, it is free and publicly available. Choose the NAM link at this website: https://mag.ncep.noaa.gov/model-guidance-model-area.php to access the model.

NAM is a regional model and not a global model. It only predicts for the United States (and parts of Canada and Mexico). While it may not be global, in the shorter term – predicting ½ a day to 3 ½ days, it can be on the whole more accurate than the global models. It currently runs four times a day.

The Canadian equivalent of the NAM, which is similarly free to the public, is the Regional Deterministic Prediction Systems, or *the RDPS Model*, which you can access through this link: https://weather.gc.ca/model_forecast/index_e.html.

Finally, the last key model to know about for forecasting snow in Colorado is *the WRF Model*, or the Weather Research and Forecasting Model, pronounced like the second word in "Fisherman's *Wharf*." I'd like to think I've saved the best for last. If I had to rank the models for how often I use them personally, the WRF Model would get the gold, the American (GFS) Model would get the silver, and either the Canadian (GDPS) or the NAM Model would get the bronze.

The WRF Model was developed at the National Center for Atmospheric Research, NCAR – in the beautiful I.M. Pei designed facility on Table Mountain sitting just above the town of Boulder, Colorado. The WRF Model is open source. It is used by various groups to create local models. Most importantly for Colorado skiers, the WRF Model forms the backbone of the Colorado Avalanche Information Center's own weather model. Run on servers in the town of Keystone, the CAIC's WRF Model currently provides point forecasts out 3 ½ days for virtually every major ski area and backcountry location in Colorado.[28] It is found at https://avalanche.state.co.us/forecasts/weather/model-forecasts/. There are actually two different

---

[28] A *point forecast* is exactly what it sounds like – a model forecast for a specific point on the map, so a person can look at a point forecast for A-Basin Ski Area, Keystone Ski Area, or many dozens of other locations throughout our mountains.

WRF models one can access through the CAIC. Choose the "CAIC WRF HiRes" from among the model options as it is the more modern one.

So now you at least know the basics of the major three medium-term global models, and the major three short-term regional models. These are not the only six models in existence, but these six are the key models for weather forecasting for Colorado's mountains. Everyone has their own favorite model products, but keeping in mind these six should be more than sufficient. Of course, as computing power increases, there are always new models coming on-line and significant changes to existing models. As such, any chapter on computer models is necessarily out-of-date not too long after it is written.

The brief descriptions I've provided so far cannot begin to describe or do justice to these weather models. However, a National Weather Service forecaster out of Juneau Alaska, in one of the great weather forecasts of all times, explained these models far better than I could ever do. In the May 13, 2014 morning forecast discussion for Southeast Alaska, the meteorologist analogized each weather model to speed dating. The forecast went as follows:

"Picking a model of choice for the day is a little like speed-dating: too little time / information to make up the mind leading to regrets by the end of the date / shift.

The American NAM is modern, detail-oriented, prolific, willing if a little impetuous and incredibly reactionary.

The American GFS – the model next door – quite old fashioned, an open book, easy on the eyes if a little staid at times. Always talking about the future while white-washing the present.

The Canadian sometimes a little pro-European sometimes a little pro-American .... Many times hard to read, but often has a sunnier outlook than the others. Too sunny sometimes.

And that European one ... intelligent, trend-setting, and alluring – only appearing twice a day – makes me want more.

And today I wanted more again so I made my selection. But sometimes I look back and wonder what could have been."

There you have it. The perfect description of the weather models. So, to sum it up:

Model	Scale	Time Scale	Speed Dating Potential Per the NWS Forecaster
The European Model	Global	Medium-term	intelligent, trend-setting, and alluring
The American (GFS) Model	Global	Medium-term	the model next door – quite old fashioned, an open book, easy on the eyes if a little staid at times, always talking about the future while white-washing the present
The Canadian (GDPS) Model	Global	Medium-term	sometimes a little pro-European sometimes a little pro-American …. many times hard to read, but often has a sunnier outlook than the others, too sunny sometimes.
The NAM Model	Regional	Short-term	modern, detail-oriented, prolific, willing if a little impetuous and incredibly reactionary
The RDPS Model	Regional	Short-term	[Just look back at the Canadian model description]
The WRF Model	Regional (for CAIC)	Short-term	[Sadly, no description in the forecast]

If the European Model is the best, you may ask, why do we need five other ones? Setting aside the facts that it's often not the most accurate one and the damn Europeans charge for it, the answer is simply that models are far more helpful to use in conjunction with each other than alone.

Fortunately, forecasters are not monogamous when it comes to choosing forecasts, and it is incredibly valuable to be able to compare these models. Forecasters don't just want a second opinion. The weather is too complicated for just two opinions. The more opinions, within limits, the better. When the six major models all disagree, the weather is fairly unpredictable. When the six major models all agree, the forecaster can be far more confident in his or her forecast. This is why so much time in forecast discussions is spent talking about whether or not the various models are in alignment. A forecaster's confidence in his or her forecast is largely dependent on whether the models are all producing generally the same results or drastically different results.

Hopefully, you're not too overwhelmed with model names, because there's another category of model worth knowing about. These are the ensemble models. Let's address ensemble models next.

Chapter 12

Ensemble Models and the Butterfly Effect

In order to understand what ensemble models are and why they exist, you need to understand *the butterfly effect*. (Heck, the butterfly effect is the elephant in the room for all weather forecasting.) Most everyone has heard of the butterfly effect, but few know what it really is. Hint, it's not the crappy 2004 movie starring Ashton Kutcher. To explain the butterfly effect, let's talk about Edward Lorenz. After getting a bachelor's degree in mathematics from Dartmouth, a master's degree in mathematics from Harvard, working as a weather forecaster for the U.S. Army Air Corps during World War II, getting a second master's degree in meteorology from MIT, and getting a PhD in meteorology from MIT – okay, he was a pretty smart guy – he became a professor at MIT. Readers of this book can forgive him for not being a downhill skier considering he lived in Boston and was at least a hiker, climber, and cross-country skier.

Lorenz in many ways was the father of computer-based meteorology, though it was an IT issue he had while working on weather models that led to him founding an entire new field of science. But I'm getting ahead of myself.

In 1961, Lorenz was modeling weather on his computer, and I'd venture to guess his computer wasn't exactly as good as our smart phones today. One day at work, he was curious to go back to a prior weather simulation he had been working on a few days earlier on his computer. However, as his computer hardly moved quickly, to save time he decided to start his model run halfway through, entering data that he had printed out from his prior run. He looked at the printout, and it listed a value as 0.506, and that's what he typed into his stimulation. He went out for a coffee while the computer did its math, (again, computers were a bit slower back then), and when he came back to check the results, something had gone very wrong. The results were completely different – the predicted weather had changed completely from when he ran the same numbers a few days earlier.

So, just like today, what did he do? He called IT, as his computer must have been malfunctioning. But as IT departments must have been as slow to respond in 1961 as they are today, as he sat waiting he decided to recheck his numbers. And that's when he found that the computer program was working the calculation out to six decimal places, and the number he was supposed to type in should have been 0.506127, even though the printout just printed to three decimal places, that is, it printed 0.506. Surely, such a tiny error in an input couldn't cause a change that completely alters the weather? But it did.

In that moment, Lorenz had discovered the butterfly effect. Using this information, he went on to found the entire scientific field of chaos theory.[29]

His discovery at the beginning, however, did not have a catchy name. Lorenz initially called it *Deterministic Nonperiod Flow*. Boring! However, in presenting his monumental discovery, one of the titles of a series of lectures given by Lorenz was: *Does the flap of a butterfly's wings in Brazil set off a tornado in Texas?* The title was just too catchy – forever the concept would be known as the butterfly effect.[30]

---

[29] Sadly, although chaos theory is arguably one of the three major breakthroughs in physics in the 20th Century – with relativity and quantum mechanics being the other two – Lorenz did not win a Nobel Prize for his extraordinary discovery and subsequent analysis. Of course, Albert Einstein also did not win a Nobel Prize for relativity, which makes you wonder why we consider the Nobel Prize to be so prestigious.

[30] The original title involved a seagull not a butterfly, but a colleague recommended the butterfly analogy. It is unknown exactly where the idea to use a butterfly as opposed to a seagull came from, but there are two likely suspects. First, a decade before Ed Lorenz's discovery, Ray Bradbury wrote a popular short

Now in all fairness, the flap of one butterfly's wings probably does not impact weather across the equator. There are too many other inputs dampening out that one input. But the point is very well taken. Seemingly insignificant changes in initial inputs can drastically change the output.

This is quite a problem if you want to forecast the weather (or any other chaotic system). Think of the problem created by the butterfly effect in this way – if your salary today is approximately $5,000 a month, and you work 12 months a year, your annual salary next year should be approximately $60,000. It could be a bit higher or a bit lower, but $60,000 is a pretty good guess. We almost always do approximations when we do math in practical settings, and like this example, these approximate answers are usually close enough to be useful. But, when it comes to meteorology (and the many other fields impacted by the butterfly effect and chaos theory), approximate inputs today do not give approximate future values. If the task of calculating your salary next year was a chaotic system (like the weather), the difference between earning $4,999 a month or $5,000 a month during this current month could make the difference between you earning $20,000 or $2,000,000 next year. How the heck do you do math when chaos invades the system?

But it gets even worse. The butterfly effect and the whole field of chaos theory not only was discovered in the context of meteorology, but it has an especially vicious effect in meteorology. This is due to the fact that it is impossible to accurately monitor enough of the inputs of a complex weather

---

story, *A Sound of Thunder*, where an unwary time traveler to the Jurassic period accidentally steps on a butterfly, causing a different future when he returns to modern times. (And, like you should avoid the 2004 movie called *The Butterfly Effect*, you should definitely avoid the 2005 movie, *A Sound of Thunder*.) Second, as part of his investigation into his discovery of the butterfly effect and the chaos theory, Ed Lorenz plotted the pattern of the chaos graphically. How do you plot the pattern of chaos, as chaos is chaotic, you might ask? Well, it's important to distinguish chaos from randomness. It's very hard to predict chaos, but chaotic systems unlike random systems do display certain patterns. One of Ed Lorenz's plots of the pattern of chaos, now called a Lorenz Attractor, looks a lot like a butterfly's wings. So, it's the perfect symbol for this powerful concept.

system. If you don't know if your monthly salary is $5,000 or $6,000, then in a chaotic system how do you predict next year's salary?

Here's an example of the problem with obtaining accurate inputs. As discussed in Chapters 5 and 8, changes in the middle and upper portions of our level of the atmosphere (i.e., the troposphere) have major impacts on weather. How do we measure the higher portions of the atmosphere? Well, our best device are weather balloons. Every morning around 6 am in the summer (and 5 am in the winter), and every evening around 6 pm in the summer (and 5 pm in the winter), the National Weather Service releases one 6-foot-wide weather balloon by the old Stapleton airport in Denver and another one in Grand Junction. Over the next two hours, each balloon climbs through the troposphere and into the stratosphere. These balloons each carry a device called a radiosonde, which as the balloon ascends measures pressure, temperature, relative humidity, latitude, and longitude. This data is relayed back to the National Weather Service, and this data forms our basic understanding of the current state of the middle and upper-level troposphere. Here's the catch, however. There are only two balloons launched in Colorado. While we have countless monitoring stations on the ground in our state – we literally only have two in the air. When you read an Upper Air Map, see Chapter 14, those are the two data points in Colorado. And they only produce data twice a day.

Frankly, Colorado gets more weather balloons than many other states. There are only 69 weather balloon daily launch locations in the continental United States. Heck, Montana only gets one weather balloon for a much larger state. So, there's a lot going on in the upper atmosphere we simply can't measure because to be blunt, it's just too expensive to be sending up balloons with sensors every hour, and from thousands of locations in the continental United States.[31]

---

[31] This is not meant to imply that the National Weather Service is cheap (it isn't) or doesn't hold up its own weight globally (it does). There are roughly a thousand weather balloons launched twice a day worldwide. And the National Weather Service carries its fair share of the weight, launching a total of 92 balloons twice a day – 69 in the continental United States, 13 in Alaska, 9 in the Pacific, and one in Puerto Rico.

But it gets worse. Remember in Chapter 2, when you were a cloud, how you were born over the Pacific Ocean? Well, it's awfully hard to send weather balloons from locations where there's no land. So, there are virtually no weather balloons over the Pacific Ocean. If one draws a triangle between the coasts of Alaska, Hawaii, and California, there is not a single weather balloon launched in that entire triangle.

What about satellites, you may ask? Satellites only provide data from looking down, just like ground monitoring stations only provide data from looking up. While they're helpful, they're no substitute for weather balloons. Airplanes from cooperating airlines help a bit more than satellites to provide data on what is occurring in the middle and upper troposphere – though they aren't as good as weather balloons. Airplanes move fast. They don't go where they're necessarily needed. They don't have as many instruments as weather balloons. And perhaps most importantly, airplanes stick to certain routes and elevations, so large swaths of the Pacific Ocean have no planes, let alone no weather balloons, providing data.

With this lack of data on middle and upper atmosphere conditions, and only extrapolating that data based upon the information we do have, it is easy to see how vicious the butterfly effect can be on forecasting weather. We simply must guess what's going on in the atmosphere above the Pacific Ocean north of Hawaii and south of the typical flight paths of planes travelling between the U.S. and Asia. What if we're merely guessing that it's .05 degrees warmer than it actually is in that thousand-mile-wide swath? Well guess what, the weather a week later could be completely different throughout the globe. Damn butterfly effect!

This is why meteorology will never have the predictive power of classical physics.[32] While we know where a solar eclipse will be a century from now

---

[32] Or perhaps all of today's greatest mathematicians and scientists who are working on chaos theory are just missing something – and some future Newton or Einstein will figure it out and make weather finally predictable. After all, Newton had to invent a new form of mathematics, calculus, in order to solve what were previously intractable and impossible physics problems. The history of scientific discoveries dictates that we should not rule out the possibility that

as we can accurately predict the sun, moon, and earth locations a hundred years away, we'll likely never be able to make an accurate weather forecast six months out, no matter how much more we learn and how much more our computing power increases. The butterfly effect means we can never measure all inputs accurately enough to know what the eventual outputs will be.

And that is what brings us back to ***ensemble models***. If you're a weather forecaster, how do you deal with chaos theory? How do you deal with the fact that the most seemingly minor change in some minor area today can result in a profound change to the weather a week from now? You embrace it by running numerous computer simulations with ever so slight initial variable changes to see what results are produced with each change. In other words, you add or subtract a few dozen butterflies and see what happens. With dozens of computer model runs of the weather, each with slight variations in the initial condition inputs, you create the ensemble of different outcomes.

Today, most models run ensemble forecasts in addition to their main forecast. One I look at is the National Weather Service's Global Ensemble Forecast System (i.e., the GEFS). It is free and available to anyone in the world. Choose the GEFS-MEAN-SPRD link at this website: https://mag.ncep.noaa.gov/model-guidance-model-area.php to access the model. Again, thank you Uncle Sam!

Another great ensemble forecast you can access for free, from the same webpage is the North America Ensemble Forecasting System (i.e., NAEFS), which pools model data from the United States, Canada, and Mexico. Thanks for sharing, neighbors! You're both way cooler than those greedy Europeans. I also sometimes look at the Canadian ensemble forecast (i.e., the GEPS) via the point forecast website https://spotwx.com.

That said, again I'm saving the best for last. One of the greatest tools available online for ensemble model forecasts comes courtesy of the University of Utah's Weather Center. If you go to http://weather.utah.edu/, choose NAEFS-Downscaled, and then choose Plumes, you can access ensemble snow forecasts for over twenty locations in Colorado. These charts show each

---

some towering genius will figure it all out. That said, I'm not holding my breath on it.

different ensemble snowfall forecast from the NAEFS ensemble runs (mentioned above) for each of these twenty locations. When there is a storm approaching, one can look at the ensemble to see the range of possibilities. Almost always, one of the runs will produce just a dusting of snow and another one will produce 40 inches of snow. But, if most model runs produce somewhere between 6 and 12 inches of snow, the best guess is that it'll snow between 6 and 12 inches. Interestingly enough, the butterfly effect never disappears, so while the 6 to 12 inch forecast is usually right, if you spend enough time in the mountains, you'll not infrequently see just a dusting (or sometimes no snow and sun) when 6 to 12 inches was predicted only a few days ago (which sucks). But, you'll also see 40 inches (or even more) of snow when only 6 to 12 inches was predicted only a few days ago (which is fricking awesome).

An ensemble model cannot eliminate the butterfly effect. But it can help show the range of possibilities and the comparative likelihood of these possibilities. The University of Utah's product is great tool as you can quickly get a sense of the highest, lowest, and rough midpoint of each ensemble run in terms of snowfall.

Even if you do not look at a specific ensemble model, by looking at the results of each of the different major non-ensemble models (for example, comparing the American (GFS) Model, the Canadian (GDPS) Model, the NAM Model, and the CAIC WRF Model), you're basically creating an ensemble model in your head. By looking at how each different model predicts a different amount of snow for the same location, you've created an ensemble, so to speak.

The models we've discussed in these two chapters are a long ways away from being perfect (and they'll likely never reach the goal of being perfect). But forecasting is steadily improving.

Computer models are the best tool we have in predicting weather. When you consider the difficulty of predicting weather in such a complex and chaotic system, with so many inputs and variables, the forecasting skill of the major computer models and their ensembles are nothing short of extraordinary. They're still far from perfect, but they're a heck of a lot better than nothing. And, they're a heck of a lot better than they were only a few decades ago.

PART 4

PREDICTING THE FUTURE (ROUND TWO): UNDERSTANDING WEATHER FORECASTING

At this point in the book, we've already covered why it snows (Part One), the micro and macro of snow and weather (Part Two), and the weather models that predict the weather (Part Three). Now it is time to put these concepts together.

Sure, one can just read a short weather forecast itself, such as the typical weather app you probably have on your phone. That forecast is likely just a weighted average of a number of different models that predicts the weather in the ski town and not on the mountain. To understand the art of forecasting, you either need to put together the information in the first three parts of the book, or rely upon a professional to do it and be able to read his or her thoughts in a forecast discussion.

This part of the book will answer several important questions. What can you do as an untrained person to try to make sense of publicly available weather information to increase your odds of hitting amazing powder days? Indeed, can you as a lay person forecast better than highly trained meteorologists? (Spoiler alert, while you probably cannot beat the experts in forecasting Colorado as a whole, you'll almost always beat the experts if you focus in on just one or two locations.) But, if forecasting yourself is too much work and you do want to rely upon the professionals, which forecasters have the best forecasts? And, if you are actually somewhere without an internet connection and thus cannot access the wonderful world of computer models, what field forecasting can you still do? Let's discuss all of these topics.

Chapter 13

Why You Should Do Home Weather Forecasting

I f (1) you have a PhD in fluid dynamics, (2) you are really good at differential equations, and (3) most importantly, the processing speed of your laptop is measured in teraflops, then perhaps you can consider sophisticated weather modeling at home. Shoot, you only fall into two of these three categories? Then perhaps it's better to leave the weather modeling to the national governments or University consortiums.

But just because you cannot at home recreate the European Model, the American (GFS) Model, or the WRF Model, don't despair. You still have access to the models. And, there are two big reasons why creating your own forecast will make you a better powder hunter.

How Your Knowledge Can Improve Upon the Model Forecast

In places that are flat, models do a pretty darn good job. Why? Because precipitation in flat places is never a result of orographic lifting. (See Chapter 2.) However, the models are less reliable in big mountains. Why?

It all comes down to the concept of resolution. The models tend to use a grid system, where they divide the world (or North America) into grid cells. The model then predicts the weather for each grid cell. The term resolution simply refers to the size of the grid. A 3 kilometer by 3 kilometer grid cell is an extraordinary narrow one for a model. (Technically grid cells are three dimensional, but that gets pretty confusing so let's stick with the two-dimensional example.) And a lot can happen within a 9 square kilometer (that is 3.5 square mile) area.

So how big are these grid cells? At the time of writing this chapter in the autumn of 2019 (which I figured is worth mentioning as grid size does shrink as computing power increases), let's take a look at the grid cells that include Arapahoe Basin in Summit County.

Let's start with the global (and freely available) computer models. The American (GFS) Model's single grid cell in which A-Basin is placed includes not only Loveland, but also Winter Park, and popular backcountry spots St. Mary's Glacier, Berthoud Pass, and Jones Pass. If you know the area, those are six rather climatically distinct popular ski areas / backcountry spots. And that's in only one grid cell! The Canadian (GDPS) Model's single grid cell in which A-Basin is placed includes not only Loveland, but also includes Keystone and extends as far out as the old and former Guanella Pass Ski Area. And the Canadian Ensemble (GEPS) single grid cell is larger than Summit County itself, encompassing not only A-Basin, Loveland, Breckenridge, Copper, and Keystone, but extends southwards beyond the 14ers of Lincoln, Cameron, Democrat, and Bross. By way of another example from a different part of Colorado, a single grid cell of both the American (GFS) Model and the Canadian (GDPS) Model includes Telluride, Silverton, and backcountry spot Red Mountain Pass.

Even if we look at the short-term regional computer models, these grid cells are still surprisingly large. Going back to A-Basin, the Canadian (RDPS) model includes all of Loveland within the same grid cell as A-Basin. The NAM model grid cell that has A-Basin includes half of Loveland and extends all the way to the Bakersville Exit on I-70. The difference between A-Basin and Loveland is fairly substantial from a snow perspective. And the difference between A-Basin and the Bakersville exit on I-70 from a snow standpoint is simply extraordinary. Yet they're all within the same computer model grid cell.[33]

---

[33]   Forecasters call these features *subgrid*, as they occur within the grid and thus cannot be accounted for (to a large degree) in the model. And as we'll see in Chapter 19, literally a four-foot fence can drastically impact snow. Talk about subgrid!

Fair warning, the rest of the footnote is probably rather boring unless you're obsessed with the region I forecast. With regards to the relatively large area that I forecast for my backcountry ski patrol – i.e., the Front Range backcountry of Boulder and Gilpin County (roughly from Rocky Mountain National Park to a little north of I-70, and from the Continental Divide to the Peak-to-Peak highway), this area constitutes less than a grid cell space on the global models. Of course, nothing is simple, and neither of the freely available global models have a grid cell squarely over the patrol area.

There are three American (GFS) Model grid cells that cover portions of the area (though spill out far in every direction). One of them is centered roughly around Nederland (averaging 9,500 feet elevation, with half of it to the east of the Peak-to-Peak). Another one is centered roughly around Twin Sisters (averaging 9,000 feet elevation, with only the southwest corner in our patrol area). The third one is centered roughly around Devil's Thumb Ranch (averaging 10,000 feet in elevation, with only the far east portion within the backcountry patrol area).

There are two Canadian (GDPS) Model grid cells that cover portions of the area, with one of them covering most of our patrol area (and beyond in every direction but south) centered around roughly Brainerd Lake (averaging 8,500 feet elevation). For the southern portion of our patrol zone, there is another grid cell that's northern third partially covers our patrol area (covering the Eldora Sidecountry / Lost Lake and East Portal Backcountry areas; and averaging 9,000 feet elevation.)

As for the regional short-term models, there are four grids cell of the NAM model I can look at for the forecasts. One covers the lower elevation East Portal area and Eldora Sidecountry / Lost Lake, and averages 9,500 feet; another one is centered on Silver Lake and covers from Caribou to the south side of Brainerd Lake and averages 9,500 feet; and a third one covers from the north side of Brainerd Lake through St. Vrain Mountain and Meadow Mountain and averages 9,500'. A fourth grid cell covers the upper elevation

But it gets worse than that. Models tend to smooth out features smaller than five grid lengths in any rate, as too much noise appears for smaller grid cells. Regardless, going to smaller grid cells requires not only far more computational power, but also far more observational stations feeding data into the models. Accurate computer modeling for a single mountain, like A-Basin, is still a long way off.

And let's not forget that most of the people who design most of the models are obsessed with the noble goal of helping mankind mitigate disasters – hurricanes, droughts, tornados, etc. – as well as providing forecasts for military purposes. Predicting how much powder will fall at each ski area in Colorado is hardly the main goal of the mathematicians working on the models. (The notable exception is the CAIC WRF Model.) So, for the foreseeable future, we must remember that the models are excellent in predicting the location of highs and lows, and but only okay in figuring out exactly where the powder will fall in the complex mountain topography of Colorado.

Let's take my beloved Berthoud Pass. For those not familiar with Berthoud Pass, it's the high mountain pass between Empire and Winter Park. Today it's all backcountry, but it used to have a ski area at which I patrolled during the second half of the 1990s. It is one of the great spots in Colorado for snow, and having spent countless days working there, and then after it closed having spent countless days backcountry skiing there, I've slowly learned the interaction between its topography and the weather.

---

of East Portal (but extends all the way to the town of Winter Park to the west), and averages 10,000 feet.

There are eight grid cells of the RDPS model I can look at for the forecasts, but six of them have very frustrating locations for forecasting. Of the two easier ones, one is roughly centered around East Portal and averages 10,000' elevation; and another one includes Eldora Sidecountry / Lost Lake and Caribou, and averages 10,000' elevation. Then, there are four grid cells that all meet and have their four-corners roughly at Brainerd Lake. The northern two of these meet two more gird cells to the north with the four corners meeting at the middle of Rock Creek.

If time was unlimited, I'd look at the point forecasts for all seventeen of these grid cells as I pulled together my forecasts. If only.

The best way to picture the Berthoud Pass terrain is to picture a ridge running from the south (at Mt. Stanley) to the north (the top of the Panorama lift at Winter Park), with a series of drainages / bowls to the east of this ridge. These drainages / bowls contain the legendary terrain, from south to north, Stanley Cirque, No Name, Current Creek, Second Creek, First Creek, and Zero Creek. Below these drainages runs Highway 40. Colorado Mines Peak and Mount Flora sit to the east of Highway 40 also providing some, if more limited, skiing.

If the wind is blowing from the north but not too strongly, the closer one is to Winter Park, the more powder there is. Why? As the moisture is hitting the base of Winter Park and is lifting causing more snow, it's going to hit Winter Park and the more northerly drainages / bowls of Berthoud Pass first. The winds at this speed (think 10-20 mph) tend not to be strong enough to get as much snow past the high pass of Berthoud Pass and its surrounding even higher mountains. There is less snow as you head southwards. So, skiing Zero Creek is better than skiing No Name drainage when the winds blow from the north. If the wind is blowing from the south but not too strongly, the situation is reversed, with the best skiing in No Name drainage and worse skiing the closer to Winter Park one moves. Why? Because under each example it dumps more as the clouds are climbing than when they are leveling off. At higher wind speeds, the spillover effect becomes more pronounced, confusing the picture. And at lower wind speeds, often the clouds won't climb enough to produce any snow.

Try to find a weather model that will explain this. It won't happen in the near future. Models tend not only to predict the same amount of snow at Berthoud Pass and Winter Park (which is not accurate), but also the same amount of snow at Loveland Pass as Berthoud Pass (which is crazy as they see drastically different totals from each snowstorm).

This is why this book is so important. It takes imagining yourself as a cloud, and visualizing your travel in order to figure out which mountain is best to ski under which conditions. The snow amounts forecasted in the models provide a guide. But to have the best shot at getting the best powder, you have to supplement them with your own knowledge of wind conditions and snow patterns to extrapolate who will get more snow.

How You Can Improve Upon the
Professional Forecasters

Now I can hear you asking, why not just rely upon the professional weather forecasters? For example, can't you just rely upon the folks at Open Snow? At CAIC? At the National Weather Service?

Don't get me wrong, they are amazing. They are in a different league of weather forecasting than me. I play in the amateur league, and they play in the professional league. And I assume you, like me, also play in the weather forecasting amateur league.

However, the professionals each have only a handful of people forecasting for a very large area. If you want to forecast whether to ski the backcountry at St. Mary's Glacier area, Berthoud Pass, or Jones Pass – in a half hour you can figure out more details than the professionals will ever provide. Why? They may be better forecasters than you, (they are certainly better forecasters than me), but you're only focusing on three exact spots. A half hour on three exact spots is far more valuable than a professional spending several hours trying to forecast one-third of the State of Colorado. Trust me, if I can figure it out, anyone can figure it out.

Hopefully with the pointers throughout the book, and the information in Appendix A, you can start to couple your own personal knowledge with this book to produce forecasts on your own. Let me walk you through my process in the next few chapters.

Chapter 14

How to Read Forecast Models and Weather Maps – A Four-Dimensional Guide

If you're new to reading forecast models, it can be a bit intimidating. Don't worry, however, with a bit of knowledge and a bit of practice, it will quickly make sense. If I can figure it out, anyone can figure it out.

Forecast models are made to be understood in four dimensions. Let's get the easy two of the four dimensions out of the way first. North, south, east, and west (or as you look at the map up, down, right, and left respectively) are the easy dimensions, and virtually every model provides either the state boundaries or the county boundaries so you can find the location about which you care. Remember on the larger models, to not mix up the big square states, Colorado with Wyoming, when looking at these maps. This is especially true when the map is of North America and not just the Continental United States, and that is where I (sorry, meant to write "one," not "I") most often can get the two big square states confused. Find the lower big square state on the map. It's the one with the four corners on your bottom left, as opposed to the upper big square state with Idaho to your left.

For the model maps broken down by county, which are always helpful, it's beneficial to learn (or at least look up on a map) the locations of the places you care about relative to county line locations. For example, below is a diagram of the legendary Summit County, which I've added arrows showing the location of its four ski areas (A-Basin, Breckenridge,

Copper, and Keystone) as well as four ski areas easily located just by using the shape of Summit County (which are Loveland, Ski Cooper, Vail, and Winter Park).

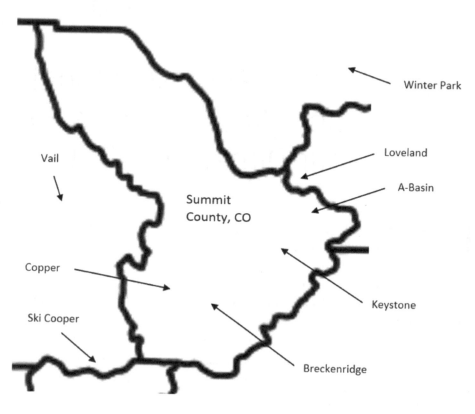

Okay, easy enough as long as you're not embarrassed to search county lines relative to location. We have two of the four dimensions down.

Instead of tackling the vertical dimension first, as it's the most complex, let's tackle the time dimension next, as it's a bit tougher but not as tough as the vertical dimension. Every global weather model wants a consistent time. And that makes sense. How can you show a large part of the globe, without using a universal time? Good thing there happens to be a universal time; but bad thing the universal time doesn't happen to be Mountain Time.

Unfortunately for us, universal time comes from England. It seems like everything comes from England. Our language, our measurement system, Shakespeare, Newton, Darwin, Churchill, the Beatles, Monty Python, fish and chips, universal time. Well, you get the point. Universal time is the time (sort of) in London. It is London Time, without daylight savings time. Universal time is also known as UTC, Greenwich Mean Time, GMT, Zulu Time, and Z.

So, if a weather map says 00 UTC or 00 Z, that means midnight Greenwich Mean Time, which is 6 pm the day before in the summer in Colorado, or 5 pm the day before in the winter in Colorado. If the map says 12 UTC or 12 Z, that means noon Greenwich Mean Time, which is 6 am that day in the summer, or 5 am that day in the winter. Yes, it's confusing, but you'll get used to it. And, for some models – for example, portions of the CAIC's WRF Model – they are (thank goodness) in Mountain Time. So, be sure to always look at the time the model is predicting, which is usually the part that says "forecast valid for XXX time," and make sure you know whether it's in universal time or mountain time. If the former, be sure to convert the time in your head.

Okay, so we now have three of the four dimensions down. North/south, east/west, and time. Now it's time (no pun intended) to address the most complicated one, the vertical dimension.

Hikers, ski mountaineers, and many other people think of the vertical dimension in terms of elevation above sea level. Denver is 5280' above sea level. Colorado's highest peak, Mt. Elbert, is 14,439' above sea level. But in weather maps, it's not elevation that's being measured. Rather, it is pressure.

1,000 millibars of pressure is roughly sea level elevation. 850 millibars of pressure is roughly the elevation of my house in Golden, i.e., 6,000' above sea level. 700 millibars of pressure is roughly the elevation of Leadville, i.e., 10,000' above sea level.

500 millibars of pressure is 18,000' above sea level, higher than any peak in Colorado – roughly a mile higher than the highest ski lift in Colorado – Breckenridge's Imperial Express. It's a bit shorter than Denali, North America's highest peak. And 300 millibars of pressure is (very) roughly the height of Mt. Everest, sitting at 29,029' above sea level.

Here's a chart:

Millibars of Pressure (hPA)	Roughly Equivalent Elevation (feet)	Rough Location Example
1,000	0'	Miami, Florida
850	6,000'	Golden, Colorado
700	10,000'	Leadville, Colorado
500	18,000'	Mount Elbrus, Russia
300	30,000'	Mt. Everest, Nepal

Why did I just throw out these five random pressure levels — 1,000 millibars, 850 millibars, 700 millibars, 500 millibars, and 300 millibars? Because most maps of the upper atmosphere measure the atmospheric conditions at these five pressure levels. These somewhat universally agreed-to standard levels were not necessarily designed for powder hunting in Colorado. The 700 millibars does a great job predicting atmospheric conditions roughly 1,000' above a 9,000' mountain (think of Granby Ranch or Hesperus). Unfortunately, however, for Colorado's higher elevation terrain, there are no charts for 650 millibars (roughly 12,000') or 600 millibars (roughly 14,000').

What do these pressure levels tell us?

300 millibars. The 300 millibar level (roughly 30,000' or 30% of the air at sea level) is the rough elevation of the jet stream. As such, the 300 millibar upper air forecast maps look at the position of the jet stream and see if there are jet streaks that may enhance snowfall. (See Chapter 5.)

500 millibars. The 500 millibar level (roughly 18,000' or half as much air as sea level) provides an excellent look at the location of troughs, ridges, and cut-off lows. Let's take ridges and troughs as an example. As discussed in Chapter 4, it's warm at the equator, and warm air expands, so the height of half the air in our atmosphere (i.e., the 500 millibar level) is relatively high. At the poles, the height of this 500 millibar level is much lower as it's cold, and cold air takes up less space than the warm air.

So, over the United States, where the height of the 500 millibar level is higher in elevation (i.e., the air from the equator is invading) you have a ridge. It's literally a ridge in the height of the air – and ridges are not good. Where the height of the 500 millibar level is lower (i.e., the air from the north pole is invading), you have a trough. It's literally a valley in the height of the air. There's less pressure at ground level. Troughs are good.

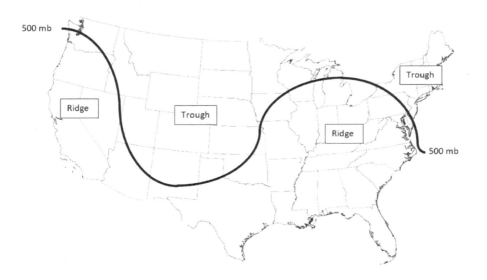

The 500 millibar upper air forecast maps are helpful to tell you whether you're in a trough or a ridge, whether a trough or ridge is headed your way, whether there is a big low pressure system developing, and whether it may close or cut-off from the trough. It also provides relative humidity predictions. Relative humidity over 70% means clouds are likely. Relative humidity over 90% means precipitation is likely. I'll discuss this more in Chapter 15.

700 millibars. The 700 millibar maps (remember, that's roughly 10,000 feet) are helpful for humidity and winds. And, as you learned in Chapters 2 and 3, the two key elements to orographic lift are moisture and winds. So, what can give you more important information than the charts with humidity and winds?

850 millibars. The 850 millibar maps are roughly the elevation of my home in Golden, Colorado. So, unless (i) you're skiing somewhere with a much lower elevation than Colorado (think Alaska), (ii) you want to know what the weather would be if you dug a big hole beneath the Colorado ski areas, or (iii) you plan to ski Red Rocks after a big upslope snowfall (which I've done), I suggest you don't waste your precious time with the 850 millibar maps.

Now, I've left out so far the most important thing the models predict. Snow. The models also provide their best estimate for snow accumulation at the ground level. But of course, take each model's predictions with a hefty grain of salt. And don't just get a second opinion – get a third or fourth opinion.

Armed with this basic knowledge of how to read model forecast maps, let's talk about how I put together a forecast.

Chapter 15

How to Put Together a Home Weather Forecast

et me walk you through how I put together a forecast – whether informally in order to decide where to ski tomorrow, or more formally for my backcountry ski patrol – and using only free resources that are publicly available.

A quick disclaimer first. I'm providing my current process. As my knowledge increases and as websites and models change, I'm sure my process will change as well. Everyone puts together a forecast a different way, and although I'm about to walk you through my process, please don't take my process as the gold standard by any means. Rather, I'm presenting my process as an example – you are Dorothy, and I'm merely lifting the curtain so you can see this particular Wizard of Oz. I make no promises whether or not you'll like what you see.

My forecast involves six steps.

Step One – Look Out the Window

Okay, I know this first step sounds obvious, but it isn't always. Before starting a forecast, you want to know what is happening now. Is it sunny or snowing? Is it hot or cold? And don't worry if your window doesn't show what's happening where you plan to ski (or to the west of where you want to ski). Webcams and weather stations provide a plethora of information on what is happening now.

Step Two – The Big Picture

Assuming I have time when putting together a forecast, after I know what's happening now, I usually start with the big picture. Frankly, this is the most complex part of the forecast I do, so when I teach my forecast process at avalanche or mountaineering classes through my ski patrol, I usually teach the next steps first so not to scare the students, and then teach this step afterwards. So, if this seems a little much, don't let it scare you. Once you're good at step three, you can return to step two.

I pull up the American (GFS) Model – not because I think it's the most reliable but rather because I like its interface the best. You can find it here: https://mag.ncep.noaa.gov/model-guidance-model-area.php.   Choose GFS. I pull up the model for the continental United States (it's abbreviated as CONUS).

My favorite portion to pull up first is the 700 millibar relative humidity / height (abbreviated as 700_rh_ht). Why 700 millibars? 700 millibars, as a reminder, is roughly 10,000 feet. I wish there was easy access to the data at 600 millibars (which is roughly 14,000 feet), but the information provided is either for 700 millibars (roughly 10,000') or 500 millibars (roughly 18,000 feet). Considering that orographic lifting is our primary snow driver (see Chapters 2 and 3), and that occurs mostly in the few thousand feet above the mountains – the 700 millibar level (roughly 10,000') seems more informative than the 500 millibar level (roughly 18,000').

This 700 millibar relative humidity / height chart shows the height of the 700 millibar level. It's the topographical map, so to speak, of the weather at 10,000'. (See Chapters 8 and 14.) Looking at this provides me with a quick sense of the model's prediction of ridges, troughs, and low pressure areas. These are, after all, are the foundation of the weather we'll see on a big scale.

The model also shows its prediction of humidity (i.e., percentage of water saturation in the air) at 10,000 feet as one of three categories – less than 70% (colored white), 70-90% (colored light green), and over 90% (colored dark green). As a rough rule of thumb, 70-90% relative humidity means clouds. And, over 90% relative humidity means snow or rain. And, the chart also contains a few other bits of data, such as the predicted wind speed and direction at 10,000 feet, which I'll glance at.

The model provides all this information from 6 hours out to 16 days out. 16 days out, of course, is in forecast fairyland (see Chapter 25), so I usually stop looking at what the American (GFS) model is predicting somewhere between 6 to 10 days out.

Coupling the model's prediction of troughs, ridges, and low pressure areas, coupled with its prediction of snowy areas (i.e., over 90% relative humidity) – I now have a general sense of its prediction of the weather over the next week. I know when the model thinks it will be stormy, what sort of storm, and when the model thinks it will be pleasant.

If I'm putting together a written forecast for my patrol, I jot down some notes – but if I'm just forecasting in my head, I can usually remember this big picture information.

Usually at this point, I move to step three. Although there are countless important additional data from just this one model – I don't have all day. I'm a busy guy! That said, if I suspect a jet streak fueled storm, I'll usually also look at the American GFS model's 300 millibar windspeed predictions (labeled as 300_wnd-ht) – which you find in the same manner as the 700 millibar relative humidity chart.

STEP THREE – POINT AND SNOW FORECASTS

Now that I have a rough sense of the big picture in my head, I move to the point forecasts. I love the private website https://spotwx.com/. Of the six major models listed in Chapters 10 and 11, spotwx.com provides access to four of them – the Canadian (GDPS) Model, the American (GFS) Model, the NAM Model, and the RDPS Model. I usually start the with the Canadian (GDPS) Model point forecast, as I just looked at the big picture with the American (GFS) Model, and I want to see how a different model is predicting the upcoming weather. Then, depending upon how much time I have, and if the storm is close enough to be predicted by the regional NAM and RDPS models, I'll check the other three models on the website.

When looking at a point forecast, I look at both each model's snowfall predictions and also the wind direction and speed predictions. While the snowfall prediction is helpful, the wind direction and speed usually give me a sense of what is going on and how much I think the concepts of orographic lifting will be playing into the storm. Also, this often tells me whether the snow will be better above or below treeline. I also often look at temperature to try to guess-timate likelihood of good snow production and the likely density of the snow.

I'll then check the CAIC WRF point forecast, found at https://ava-lanche.state.co.us/forecasts/weather/point-forecasts/. Of the models avail-able on this webpage, the CAIC WRF HiRes is the one to choose. As discussed in Appendix G, this is my favorite model. I go through the same process in reading this point forecast. Finally, assuming I have time, I'll go to Pivotal Weather, which has some of the European Model information, and check the European Model on snowfall.[34]

Usually while I do this, I take notes of the snowfall predictions. For il-lustrative purposes, here are what the models predicted on March 17, 2020 for a storm two days later on March 19, 2020 for the points and/or cell grids for Eldora:

24" – WRF Model
16" – NAM Model
12" – Canadian Model
10" – American Model
9" – European Model

In other words, the model range was between 9-24" of snow. For what it is worth, 12" of snow ended up falling.

For another illustrative example, on March 2, 2020, the three global models were predicting the following for a storm on March 8-10, 2020 for the grid cells over Eldora, that is 6-8 days ahead of time.

10" – Canadian Model
4" – American Model
3" – European Model.

---

[34]   Using this and many similar snowfall tools, which only show county lines on their maps, one quickly learns the shapes of the key Colorado counties and where the ski areas / backcountry spots are relative to county lines.

In other words, the model range was between 3-10" of snow. Sadly, only a dusting ended up falling from this storm.

If the University of Utah has a nearby NAEFS-Downscaled ensemble point forecast (see Chapter 12), I'll check that as well. As there is not one near Eldora, these above examples do not include that ensemble run.

STEP FOUR – THINK

Okay, step four is a tough one for me. At this point, I have to think through the information I've digested. I try to approach this by thinking through the issues discussed in the first part of this book. What is causing the air to rise? How much will orographic lifting, jet streaks, low pressure, etc. play into the snowfall we're likely to see? Are the temperatures likely to mean awesome large and light snow crystals, heavy spring-like snow, or something else? Do the snowfall predictions make sense based upon the larger scale weather patterns? Do the smaller scale predicted winds favor orographic lifting for the precise spot I'm planning to go? Does the model prediction match my experience with the area?

This is the phase in which I'll often decide whether I want to go back-country skiing at Berthoud Pass, Jones Pass, Loveland Pass, or St. Mary's. Often the decision will be even more specific – based upon the direction of the storm, the type of storm, and the winds – it might impact which drainage on Berthoud Pass I choose to ski that day.

That said, thinking is a challenge. They say that weather forecasting is one-third art, one-third science, and one-third voodoo. I'll be the first to admit that I struggle with the art, I struggle with the science, and I struggle with the voodoo.

STEP FIVE (OPTIONAL) – WRITE IT UP

If I'm creating a forecast for my ski patrol (as opposed to just figuring out where or when I want to ski), I have to write up the forecast in an intelligible (although usually grammatically questionable) manner.

I always say that a good forecast discussion is 75% news and 25% editorial. I figure the readers don't care as much about what I think as what I've observed from reviewing the models. I'm not creating the forecast, but rather I'm reporting on what the models have created. So, I try to accurately report what they're predicting. As the models rarely if ever predict the typical forecasts of 1-3", 2-4", 3-6", etc., I don't label snowfall in that manner. Rather, I tend to provide each model's number and give the range amongst the models.

Then, either at the end of the forecast or sprinkled throughout it, I have my editorials – for example, I might remind the reader that this type of storm tends to be a big snow producer, or that during this time of the year, this type of storm tends not to produce a lot of snow. And, if I'm reporting on model forecasts in forecast fairyland, I always feel obliged to remind the reader of that. I provide my thoughts, but I don't think the focus should be diverted too much from the actual model data.

STEP SIX – COMPARE RESULTS WITH PREDICTIONS

Okay, while step four (i.e., thinking) might sound tough on your mind, step six is tough on your ego. If you want to improve your forecasting, you must be brutally honest with yourself. How much snow fell, versus how much did you expect? I've certainly apologized to my ski buddies half-way up the first skin of the day, realizing that while I thought there was going to be 6-10 inches of snow, it seems pretty clear there was only 3 inches of new snow.

What's important is not whether you are right or wrong – you're predicting the future after all! What's important is what did you learn from comparing the prediction to what actually happened. I learn from every storm. And, by way of a big example of my own errors, in an earlier draft of this book I relegated the concept of jet streaks to being part of the chapter on fronts and convection. I just didn't think jet streaks were important enough to warrant a lengthy description. However, underpredicting multiple jet streak fueled storms and seeing how much snow they dumped made me realize that jet streaks warrant their own full chapter.

For my patrol forecasts, so long as there was snow between my last forecast and this forecast, I always write up a retrospective discussion comparing the actual results with the models' predictions and my thoughts. Having reduced to writing the forecast from the prior week and posted it online, if I was really wrong, there's no avoiding it. It's easy to whitewash in your head a bad forecast after the fact if you didn't write it down, but not possible if it's still up on the website.

Put another way, if you have a fragile ego – don't do your own weather forecasting – it'll destroy your self-pride. But, if you're mentally tough, you don't take yourself too seriously, and you're ready to be brutally frank with yourself, you will learn a ton.

SAVING TIME TIPS

This six-step process may sound like a lot of work, but it takes less than an hour, which includes my time trying to edit the forecast to be vaguely readable and not too embarrassing from a grammatical standpoint. I almost always fail at the latter task.

If I'm just forecasting for myself, and I skip steps two, five, and six – I can usually do the whole process in five minutes and all from my phone.

That said, it's easy to get side-tracked while putting together a forecast. There are endless weather resources available, but we all only have a limited time to come up with our off the cuff predictions (or even my more formal forecasts for my fellow ski patrollers). So, instead of getting bogged down in too much data, it's important to understand the key pieces and not spend too much time on others.

Below is a list of interesting weather data, those shining glittery objects vying for my attention, but that I almost always ignore:

- Radar. I'm going to let you in on a poorly kept secret. Radar sucks in the mountains. Radar works on line-of-sight. Line-of-sight works well in Kansas. It doesn't work well in Colorado, mountains block radar. And, there aren't terribly many weather radar spots in Colorado, which is compounded by the fact that the darn earth is curved, not flat, so the radar heads off towards outer space. (Sorry flat earth types, the earth is actually round. Otherwise, radar would work way better.) If hypothetically snow fell from the top of the troposphere, then radar would still work. However, most snow forms and falls in the few thousand feet above where you're skiing. Radar at 25,000' or 35,000' above you does no good in predicting snow.

Radar is great for predicting tornadoes. It's pretty good at predicting hail. But, for snow in Colorado, radar is not worth your time.

- Satellite imagery. Satellite imagery is way better than radar in the mountains. But, its data is already incorporated into the weather models. And there are lots of problems with satellite imagery. On the visible spectrum, the satellite doesn't help at night because it's dark. During the day, clouds look like snow. And, who cares about the top of clouds anyway? I care about the snow coming from the middle of the cloud. While satellite imagery does provide water vapor information, it tends to show what occurs higher in the atmosphere than the orographic water vapor we care about. And in any event, the relative humidity charts of the models are far more helpful. Don't get me wrong, satellite imagery can be helpful. I just don't think it's worth my valuable time as I put together a forecast.

- Vorticity. Vorticity is the measure of spin. Spin creates lift. If you're drinking beer out of a cup or mug, take a spoon and swirl the beer. You'll see that the beer in the center of the cup or mug gets lower. That means there's less pressure where the spin in the greatest. Or, you can see the same principle when you pull the drain on a bathtub − spin creating lower pressure in the water directly above the drain. Spin creates low pressure. Low pressure creates lift. And lift creates snow. So, why don't I care about vorticity? Colorado's snow is mostly from orographic lifting. So, while I do pay attention to jet streaks as they're simple to understand and throw unpredictability into my forecasts, I tend to ignore vorticity. I'm sure vorticity is important. But I'm a busy guy!

- Other models. There are lots of weather models out there that I haven't discussed. I try to stick to the six I've discussed, so as not to get too overwhelmed. I'll occasionally check the HRRR (High Resolution Rapid Refresh) or UKMET, but I simply do not use the HRDPS, RAP, SREF, the ICON, or the many other alphabet soup models that are available online.

I bet with a few weeks of practice reading weather maps and model forecasts, coupled with even a basic understanding of your local topography, you'll be able to make good forecasts for yourself.

Armed with a little knowledge, you'll be ahead of the thermodynamics PhD scientist with incredible math skills who has two super computers at his disposal when it comes to forecasting. After all, he's in Reading England working on the European Model's weather forecasting, and you're the ski boots on the ground in Colorado checking many different models.

Happy forecasting!

Chapter 16

Professional Weather Forecasting

I f you don't have time to create your own forecast, it's nice to have others who you can rely upon. And even if you're creating your own forecasts, it's still great to hear the thoughts of the experts.

Fortunately, in Colorado there are a number of highly trained folks (usually who love to ski) who, based upon not only their training as forecasters, but also their long experience watching what happens after their predictions, make professional forecasts that are available to us.

Here is a quick description of the three most popular sources, in descending order of readability from a layman's perspective.

Open Snow (https://opensnow.com/dailysnow/colorado) – In 2007, a meteorologist living in Boulder named Joel Gratz started emailing powder forecasts to his friends and network. His email forecasts quickly became quite popular, and after a few iterations, Open Snow was created. Open Snow has become the go to source for the majority of skiers in Colorado who are searching out where and when to find powder.

During regular ski season, Joel provides daily snow forecasts for Colorado. And, along with fellow meteorologist Sam Collentine, they provide daily snow forecasts for various specific locations within Colorado. Open Snow also has a network of meteorologists in the United States providing forecasts for many other mountainous regions.

The value of Joel and Sam's forecast discussions cannot be overstated.

They both write easily readable and non-technical forecasts with the main goal of helping Colorado skiers find powder. When people ask me who writes my favorite forecast discussions, I don't hesitate before I say Joel Gratz. He writes the easiest to read and most educational weather forecasts for beginners to the weather world. He has the introspection to be constantly evaluating his past forecasts in order to improve his product in the future, and he's honest about missed calls. He also is always throwing in nuggets of wisdom into his forecast discussions for folks like me, who know a fair amount but always want to learn more.

Read Open Snow's forecasts. And, support them by getting an All-Access account. Thank you Joel and Sam!

CAIC (https://avalanche.state.co.us/forecasts/weather/zone-forecast/) – The Colorado Avalanche Information Center is an indispensable organization that forecasts avalanche conditions for CDOT, ski areas, and the general public. It investigates avalanche accidents, and it provides avalanche education and resources to both professionals and nonprofessionals. As Colorado leads the nation in avalanche fatalities, understanding avalanche science is critical, especially for backcountry enthusiasts.

As part of CAIC's services, not only do they provide a WRF model discussed in Chapter 11, they also offer forecast discussions written by their trained professionals twice a day during regular ski season. These forecast discussions are usually limited in time, predicting the weather only 36 hours into the future, but sometimes with references further into the future when it looks like weather will maintain itself (for better or worse) for a while. The forecast discussions from the CAIC are more technical than those from Open Snow, but if you've made it this far in the book, you should have no problem understanding them.

National Weather Service (https://forecast.weather.gov/) – The National Weather Service is the repository of numerous models, already discussed. The National Weather Service provides custom forecasts for square 2.5 kilometers grid cells for every part of Colorado. The National Weather Service sends up the weather balloons, collects the data, and provides all of the information they collect for free. And, as if that's not enough already, they also provide three forecast discussions for Colorado. Now make no mistake, these forecast discussions have been fairly described before as written by meteorologists for meteorologists. That said, I love to read them anyhow.

The National Weather Service divides the state by county (largely by water drainage areas) into the three sets of forecasts. One forecast discussion is based out of the Boulder/Denver office, one is based out of Grand Junction office, and one is based out of the Pueblo office. The exact location of the zones can be a bit confusing. Summit County (with Breckenridge and Copper) technically falls within the Boulder/Denver office, Eagle County (with Vail and Beaver Creek) technically falls within the Grand Junction office, and Lake County (with Ski Cooper) technically falls within the Pueblo office. So, it's important to know which region you're looking for, but often reading more than one of the technical forecast discussions can be helpful. When you're on the specific weather page for your region on the National Weather Service's website, click on "Forecast Discussion," and dive in.

This forecast discussion's focus, unsurprisingly, is not on powder skiing. Rather, the forecast discussions are meant to provide guidance for the media to report on weather, for the state to decide on road closures and conditions, etc. However, they do include a discussion of both weather patterns and likely snowfall amounts. And, their meteorologists are top notch with extraordinary experience. And some of their meteorologists are powder hunters like you and me. Having read the book to this point, you should already be proficient enough to comprehend a majority of each forecast discussion, especially since most technical words have links to their definitions. But they're not an easy and light read, like Open Snow.

Like every profession, forecasters have their own lingo. I've been trying to slowly (and hopefully rather painlessly) introduce this lingo throughout the book so if you are new to the language, it doesn't become too overwhelming. One trick in reading the more technical forecast discussions is to remember, for our (only slightly simplified) purposes, there are many synonyms for low pressure and many synonyms for high pressure systems. Here they are:

Low Pressure (usually means snow)	High Pressure (usually means no snow)
Cyclonic	Anticyclonic
Counterclockwise	Clockwise
Convergence (at ground)	Divergence (at ground)
Positive vorticity advection	Negative vorticity advection
Depression	

So, if you hear the terrifyingly complicated "positive vorticity advection," don't worry, that just means the forecaster is talking about a low pressure.

OTHER OPTIONS

Even though I list only three sources, there are other forecast discussion weather resources available in Colorado. I am a huge fan of Seth's Weather Report put out by Seth Linden on Facebook. Indeed, over the whole year I probably spend more time on Seth's Facebook page than any of the other sources I wrote about above.

Another resource is https://powderchasers.com, which forecasts snow all over the western half of North America focusing on the best spots to ski. Or, if you want to have a forecast to make fun of, you can always check out my own non-professional weekend forecasts (specifically geared towards my backcountry ski patrol) at: https://bmnsp.org/weather-forecast/, assuming I'm still writing it when you read this book.

In sum, if you're new to these resources, Open Snow is the easiest website to read for weather amateurs and the most oriented to finding powder. However, like models, it's good to get a second and third opinion, and many dedicated powder chasers want more of a technical discussion of what is going on in the atmosphere. CAIC's forecast is more technical, and having made it this far in this book, you should have no problem understanding it. It is geared towards avalanche conditions, so it's very helpful for hunting powder (and also staying relatively safe). The National Weather Service's forecast discussion is the most technical and the least geared towards skiers, but it is still a great resource, especially if you want a more thorough handle of the upcoming weather from a technical standpoint.

Thank you to all the professional forecasters who make our task of finding powder easier!

Chapter 17

Field Weather Forecasting

L et's leave the world of an internet connection for a few minutes and discuss field weather forecasting. Every experienced hiker knows that the best and safest forecasters for thunderstorms are their own two eyes. Often a peak is not worth trying to summit on some summer days even after setting out based upon a forecast of low or no thunderstorm danger, because the thunderheads are growing faster than predicted. Likewise, every experienced backcountry skier knows that it's their own observations — from recent avalanche activity, to shooting cracks, to how deep they're sinking into the snow — that provide the highest level of information on avalanche danger.

Field weather forecasting for predicting powder is a bit different. Once you've chosen where to ski and possibly have lost cell reception, what difference does it make whether it keeps snowing for 2 hours or for 8 hours? You can use your knowledge of how the storm came in and what happened with the winds to fine-tune where you'll ski, but you're largely at the mercy of the weather that has already happened.

That said, it may be helpful during a week-long hut trip to be able to make field weather forecasts (i.e., forecasting weather without the benefit of an internet connection). A hut trip is one of the only times that a skier in Colorado will have more than 8 hours without an internet connection to check the weather. So, let's discuss a few of the key pointers to predicting weather in the field without an internet connection. Let's start with your eyes and nose.

Eyes and Nose – It's hard to predict weather more than a few hours out based upon your field observations. Here are some tools, but bear in mind you'd be far better relying upon the weather models, even with all their weaknesses, if you had cell service.

Let's start with the biggest snow producer, orographic lifting. As you've read many times already, orographic lifting is a result of lots of moisture in the air and wind lifting the moisture over the mountain. Mountains afford a visual advantage when you are at high elevation. Sometimes, you can literally see the snowstorm approaching. Watch for the billowing clouds within a few thousand vertical feet of the mountain moving towards you. Judge if they're coming from the right direction to produce adequate lift. Don't forget to pay attention to wind direction, and when in doubt, assume the weather will move in from the west. (Once it's snowing and with a full cloud-cover, beware of what mountaineers call the "sucker hole," a little circle of blue sky in the middle of an otherwise cloudy sky. More often than not, this sucker hole is just to sucker you into falsely assuming the weather will clear.)

Before you can see the storm, it's much tougher to predict whether a storm is approaching. The most common method of trying to guess is to look at jet contrails. Jet contrails can tell you general wind patterns in the upper atmosphere, as well as the humidity in the upper atmosphere.

Much like the cloud that forms from your breath on a cold day, jet engines release hot water vapor (and a variety of other exhaust materials) into the cold upper atmosphere air. The water vapor typically condenses and forms a miniature cirrus cloud called a *jet contrail*. As an aside, as a very general rule of thumb, if the contrail doesn't form, or is only thin and short lived, it means there is not much humidity in the upper atmosphere which suggests fair weather. On the other hand, if the contrail is wide and long-lasting, that suggests that stormy weather may be approaching. Likewise, the movement of the contrails and the high clouds in the atmosphere can show which way the upper atmosphere winds are blowing. Coupled with your knowledge from Chapters 5 and 8, this may provide some clues on the approaching weather patterns.

Let's move to the other snow producing methods, (see Chapters 4-6) starting with fronts. Cold fronts are rather abrupt as the attack angle of a cold air mass is steep, so they're hard to field forecast. However, the gentle attack angle of a warm front provides more visual cues of its approach. There is an old saying: "Rings around the moon means it's going to snow soon." The halo around the moon (or the sun) is a result of light refracting from ice-crystals in high-level cirrus clouds. These clouds can indicate that a warm front is coming in. All cirrus clouds (those are the very high wispy clouds), especially if they're thickening, suggest a warm front may be approaching. Likewise, similar or more billowy clouds in the middle of the atmosphere (altocumulus and altostratus) may mean the warm front is getting closer. That said, these are hardly reliable predictors.

When winds are blowing from an unusual direction (in other words, a direction not from the western half of the compass – this is likely an indication of either a high pressure system (to your north) or a low pressure system (to your south). While the low pressure system is the bigger snow producer on average, if you're near the continental divide, or especially to the east of the continental divide, winds from the easterly half of the compass (even if coming from high pressure) often mean snow. I discussed this in Chapter 4. And, while your visual observations often tell you the wind direction, don't forget about your nose. If you're near the front range, and you smell the awful smell of the hog farms on the eastern plains, you just picked up one of the key telltale signs of an impending upslope storm. Why? Because the prevailing wind direction is to the west in Colorado – pushing the hog farm smell towards Kansas, not towards the mountains of the front range. So, if you smell the hog farms, that means the wind is blowing from the east. More than half the time I smell the hog farms in Golden, that means snow the next day.

Convective snow forms the same way thunderstorms form. So, look for the development of thunderheads (i.e., cumulonimbus clouds), the very tall, dark, billowing clouds. But remember to be careful – those are usually a sign to head indoors.

For what it's worth, two of the five snow producers – cold fronts and jet streaks – almost never reveal themselves until they're just about on you. So, I don't think it's even worth spending time on trying to predict them from the field.

Nevertheless, the best weather observations are the ones you are making about current conditions, not likely future conditions. The mountain-side areas from which wind transports snow are called *fetches*. And fetches being devoid of snow tells you that it's been windy. If it snowed recently, and there's still a ton of snow on the trees, that tells you that it hasn't been windy. You can look at cornice and pillow sizes compared to the last trip to also get a sense of recent wind activities. And of course, there's nothing like looking at a slope to guesstimate how much new snow has fallen on it.

Forecasting future weather more than a day or a day and a half out in the field is nearly impossible. There is one easy device you can carry that may help you a touch more. And that's the barometer, discussed next.

Barometer – On one of the cave tours of Glenwood Caverns in Glenwood Springs, the tour guides explain that every morning when they open the airtight door to the cave, they instantly know what the day's weather will be. When they open the door, if the wind blows out of the cave, that means weather will be bad that day. And if the wind blows into the cave, that means the weather will be good.

How does this work? Simple. Unless the door is open, the cave always stays at a constant temperature, humidity, and pressure. So, when the door is opened, if the pressure is low (meaning stormy) outside, the wind blows out of the cave. And if the pressure is high (meaning pleasant weather) outside, the wind blows from outside the cave to inside the cave.

While you may not have a cave handy to check the weather on your next hut trip, presumably someone in your group will have at least an altimeter. And, an altimeter and a *barometer* are basically the same thing. They simply measure air pressure.

If your watch has both a barometer and altimeter, it's pretty simple to see the trend in barometric pressure based on the barometer feature. Above roughly 1020 millibars in a properly calibrated barometer usually means high pressure. Below 1005 millibars generally means low pressure. But more important than the number is the change in the number. If the pressure is rapidly falling, that means a storm is likely coming in. If it's rising, good weather is headed your way.

If you only have an altimeter and not a barometer, the rule is still pretty simple. If you wake up and your altimeter says you've gained elevation overnight, that literally just means (unless you're a heck of a sleepwalker) that the pressure is falling. After all, the higher you go, the less pressure there is. If your altimeter gains elevation overnight, that means stormy weather is likely to be coming. If you wake up at a lower elevation than you went to sleep, that means the pressure is rising and you're likely in for a spell of good weather.

This of course does not just apply to overnight. If you're not changing altitude, the same rules apply to the altimeter as the barometer (as they're both measuring the same thing – air pressure), rapid increases in elevation on the altimeter without climbing in elevation means a storm is likely coming in. Now bear in mind there are many snowfalls I've seen without an accompanying drop in pressure. A barometer is not the American (GFS) Model, but I suppose it's better than nothing.

Weather Radio – When you are beyond cell tower coverage, the National Oceanic and Atmospheric Administration (NOAA) runs a repeating radio forecast with hazard warnings. The repeating radio weather reports have pretty good coverage in the Colorado Mountains, but it's coverage certainly does not expand over all of Colorado's mountains. If you want to carry a radio in the backcountry, remember that these weather radio forecasts require a special radio receiver. For more information, check out www.nws.noaa.gov/nwr/.

To wrap up this chapter, I should put in a reminder. Just because this chapter is shorter than some other chapters, I do not want to downplay the importance of paying attention to weather while you ski. Of course, it's important to pay attention to the weather. No weather forecast predicts thunderstorms nearly as accurately as your own eyes. No weather forecast can tell you as accurately as your own eyes and feelings whether you may get frostbite.

Sometimes you should put down your damn phone and trust your eyes. Just don't trust them on what weather will occur three days from now.

PART 5

UNDERSTANDING SNOW
ON THE GROUND

Snow falls from the sky. But you don't ski the sky. You ski the snow once it is on the ground. So, it is almost fair to claim that understanding when and where snow falls from the sky is only half the equation when trying to figure out how to hunt for powder.

What happens once the snow falls – or what happens in those few feet before the snow finishes its descent to the ground – is absolutely critical. A single obvious example, which has skunked almost everyone reading this book, will suffice. Ever woken up to a foot of fresh powder being reported, took the lift (or skinned) above treeline, and found there's no powder? And, immediately you know what happened – too much wind blew the foot of fresh powder away. Fortunately, the opposite occurs almost as frequently. That same foot of fresh powder that fell is suddenly two feet deep when you're skiing on the skier's left side of a north facing couloir.

In the end, we of course only care about what the powder feels like to ride, not what the snow report says. So, let's start this part of the book with understanding what a ski area and a Snotel's snow report does and does not mean. Next, and most critical, understanding surface winds and how they transport snow is essential to finding great powder. And then there's the magical powder that's created not in the clouds, but in the snowpack itself, called recycled powder. We'll explore how recycled powder forms to understand how to locate this miraculous snow. Finally, we'll explore man-made snow in all its forms – it's not just snow guns after all – as ski areas use snow fences, grooming, cloud seeding, as well as snowmaking to augment the gifts of mother nature and the wind.

Chapter 18

You Don't Ski the Snow Stake

The major textbook on mountain meteorology – Roger Barry, *Mountain Weather and Climate* – spends many pages discussing the problems with accurately measuring snowfall. But you don't need to be in a college level class to understand the problem – you've doubtlessly seen it before at ski areas. A snow report is literally a single number for new snow for the entire resort, but it doesn't snow a uniform amount from one end of the ski resort to the other end of the ski resort. The amount of snow that fell at the top of the Imperial Express Superchair just shy of 13,000 feet in Breckenridge is going to be far greater than the amount of new snow at the bottom of the Quicksilver Superchair in the town of Breckenridge at 9,600 feet. But just a little bit of wind makes the powder on some runs deeper and other runs shallower. So, will the massive amount of newly fallen snow at the top of Imperial lift all be blown away, leaving comparatively more fresh snow near the base of Quicksilver?

So, how and where do ski areas measure snowfall for their snow report? I think my experience at the now-closed Berthoud Pass ski area should help enlighten the issue. First and foremost, you must put your measurement site / snow stake somewhere with relatively easy access for patrol. This is especially important as you're doing the report around 6 am. But the easy access location must be simultaneously blocked off from guest access.

You don't want your measurement site / snow stake in a low snowfall location, as you don't want to be reporting less snow than you actually received. The marketing folks don't like that. But you also don't want to place it in your biggest snowfall location either – which we always joked about doing but never did. Why do you not want to put the snow stake at the best snow accumulation spot on the mountain? Two reasons. First, because skiers are not stupid. If you're reporting 6" and it's skiing on most of the mountain like 3", your guests are going to be angry. And they won't trust the snow reports anymore. Most ski areas are very honest, and powder skiers quickly learn which are the few ski areas who are not. Second, we reported our data daily to the Colorado Avalanche Information Center (CAIC). They needed real information, not inflated information.

Finding the right measurement site / snow stake location gets trickier. If the location is too far from trees, the wind blows snow off-of-it (or occasionally onto it). If it's too deep into the trees, however, the trees block the snowfall. And when it's snowing with a strong crosswind, how do you capture the falling / blowing snow on the snow stake? And do you measure it in a flat spot (when no one skis flat spots), or do you measure it on an angled slope? If you measure it on an angled slope, which aspect do you choose, how do you keep poachers from skiing through your site, and do you measure vertically or perpendicular to the base of the snow stake? Hopefully, these questions make it readily apparent that there are no perfect answers. The reality simply is that there's no perfect snow stake location / position that accurately represents the whole mountain.

The automated electronic measuring sites have every single one of the same issues (except for the fear of possible overreporting for marketing purposes). The most common automated snow sensors are the **SNOTEL** *sites* (which stands for SNOpack TELemetry). The Snotel sites are at least as unreliable as the hand measured reports, if not more so. Unlike the hand measured sites, the Snotel sites sometimes have technical difficulties and wild reporting errors. Do you remember reading in the news about how some poor woman in Italy got a speeding ticket for driving 437 mph? And to add insult to injury, she got this ticket not while driving some high performance and astronomically priced vehicle, like a Bugatti, but rather while driving a Ford Focus. Snotel sites make crazy errors sometimes, just like the radar machine that clocked a Ford Focus driving at the speed of a jet airplane. And, even without the occasional nutty error, Snotel sites have all the same problems of choosing the location that the hand measured sites have. If you compare ski resort webcams of their snow-stakes (probably the most reliable information on snow amounts), with the equivalent Snotel data, you can quickly see that the Snotel automated reports often don't get it right.

If you are reading the Snotel data, for what it's worth, historically I have found the Snotel's SWE (i.e., snow water equivalent) numbers to be far more reliable than their snowfall numbers. The snow water equivalent number is simply the amount of water you'd get if you melted the newly fallen snow – so if you melt 10 inches of snow and it becomes 1 inch of water, you have an SWE of 1 inch. When reading the SWE numbers, I'll take the SWE number and multiply it by 12 to get an approximation of snowfall. So, for half an inch of SWE, the formula is 0.5 inch SWE x 12 = 6 inches of snow and 1.0 inch SWE x 12 = 12 inches or 1 foot of snow. This of course is just to keep the math simple and is fairly close to our average winter storm of roughly 8% moisture content.[35]

Simply, I trust snow stake webcams more than Snotel data. But, it is important to understand that neither can ever be perfectly accurate or representative of what you plan to ski.

As an aside, can you imagine the poor weather forecaster in light of the myriad of issues pointed out above? If we cannot accurately say the snowfall total from the past storm, how does the forecaster try to figure out the next storm snowfall total? And, those who build weather models face the exact same problem. Thinking about it gives me nightmares about the flapping of butterfly wings.

Don't get me wrong. Snow stakes, Snotel sites, and webcams are all a heck of a lot better than nothing. They give us a decent idea of what the snow will be like. You can use them as a source of the hopefully somewhat

---

[35] To be a bit more precise, per the amazing Jim Steenburgh's book, *the Greatest Snow on Earth*, the average water content is 7.2% at Steamboat Springs, 7.5% at Red Mountain Pass, and 7.6% at the Eisenhower Tunnel. However, as discussed more in Chapter 22, Wolf Creek Pass averages 10.3%.

This calculation should be changed depending upon the type of storm. For a heavy spring storm of 12% water content, I divide the SWE number by 0.12, so a 0.5 inch SWE ÷ 0.12 = roughly 4 inches of snow.

average conditions at the mountain. But, the only way to really know how much powder is at any spot is to ski it yourself. After all, you don't ski the snow stake.

If not already abundantly clear, understanding wind transport of snow often helps you figure out where to find the deepest snow. So, we'll turn to this crucial powder hunting topic next.

Chapter 19

Wind, Powder Loading, and the Snow Fence Effect

U nderstanding wind is key to understanding where to ski. So, hang on (no pun intended) as we explore the wind transport of snow.

WHY WIND MATTERS

Let's begin with the importance of wind. Take out your altimeter (which is probably now on your phone) and stand almost anywhere in August in Colorado at exactly 11,000 feet. 11,000 feet, for reference, is 200 feet higher than the parking lots at Loveland and A-Basin and 300 feet lower than the parking lot at the summit of Berthoud Pass. South of I-70, you'll almost certainly be below treeline. And no matter where you go for the thousands of miles of terrain on either side of I-70, right at 11,000 feet in the month of August you will not run into snow. With one exception.

St. Mary's Glacier, roughly ten miles northwest of Idaho Springs, Colorado, sits at 11,000 feet. It is far and away Colorado's most popular "glacier" because of its proximity to Denver, the short hike (less than two miles roundtrip), and its low elevation. (Is it fair to call it a glacier? We'll discuss this in Chapter 29.)

Why is St. Mary's Glacier where it is? It certainly isn't because it snows a ton at St. Mary's Glacier. Don't get me wrong, it certainly snows at St. Mary's Glacier. It's a great backcountry spot after a good upslope storm. But no one would ever compare the total snowfall at St. Mary's Glacier to the total snowfall at the nearby Berthoud Pass, let alone Colorado's snowiest spot with accessible skiing – Wolf Creek. While there are no reliable snow gauges near St. Mary's Glacier, I'd hazard to guess it sees roughly a third of the snow that Wolf Creek sees in an average year.

So why is Wolf Creek without snow in August while St. Mary's Glacier has permanent snow that extends nearly down to tree-line? The answer is largely due to one word. Wind.

If you ever go to St. Mary's Glacier in the middle of winter, the weather most likely will be miserable. The glacier is windy! And for the reasons I'll explain in a little bit, even though you might think the glacier is miserable, the second you climb above it in the winter, the wind is even worse. The wind howls on and above the upper reaches of St. Mary's Glacier, drifting in and compacting endless snow from the higher reaches of James Peak (13,294'), Kingston Peak (12,147'), and the other surrounding mountains.

Ironically, although Colorado's peaks reach to well-over 14,000 feet, Colorado's permanent snowfields do not sit at the very tops of Colorado's highest mountains. Winds tend to blow snow from these mighty peaks, especially the ones near the Front Range, transporting snow to pockets on the lee (downwind) sides of the mountains. Colorado's glaciers tend to sit lower in elevation, usually in protected cirques, (hence why they're sometimes called Cirque Glaciers), where the winds can do their work depositing snow. Arapahoe Glacier, Colorado's largest glacier (which unfortunately is not accessible – damn you Boulder Watershed), is between the elevation of 12,100 and 13,200'. Andrews Glacier, Colorado's second largest glacier (which is accessible – thank you Rocky Mountain National Park), is even lower, between the elevation of 11,400 and 12,000'. Saint Mary's Glacier, probably Colorado's smallest named glacier, is also the lowest named glacier at 10,800 to 11,200'. And, all these glaciers form not where the snow is the deepest, but where the wind is the strongest upwind of the glaciers.[36] Wind has a profound effect on snow location.

---

[36] Now we shouldn't confuse where they form (which is almost entirely due to wind) from how big they'll be during any particular summer. While wind is the key factor in Colorado glacier formation, the relative size of the glacier year-by-year is dependent almost entirely upon the quantity of spring snows and

Are you convinced yet that it's important to understand wind? Well, if somehow St. Mary's Glacier sitting the equivalent of 200 feet above the Loveland parking lot didn't impress you, how about this. If you don't understand wind, then you may miss out on that 2" snowfall that skis like a foot because you found the right pockets of wind deposited snow. That's fine, you can be left out.

UNDERSTANDING WIND TRANSPORT OF SNOW

As discussed in Chapter 4, wind is air moving. Why does air move? Well, the textbook answer is that air is moving from areas of higher pressure to areas of lower pressure. This is of course correct, and to go back to my farting analogy in Chapter 4, everything (whether smell molecules or air masses) moves from areas of higher concentration to areas of lower concentration. But to simply say that wind is a result of moving from higher pressure to lower pressure is only part of the story. Gravity influences wind – creating challenges for an air mass moving over a mountain, and helping it on its route down. The rotation of the earth has an effect on wind – after all that's what causes wind to blow from west to east in the mid-latitudes like Colorado, and that's what causes wind to flow clockwise out of a high pressure and counterclockwise into a low pressure. Inertia plays its part too. And, the shape of the ground has a tremendous effect on wind. To understand wind, you cannot look at any one variable alone. Rather, you must look at the whole picture. But for our purposes the most important piece is the interplay between terrain and wind, because that's what determines on the small scale of the ski area at which you are skiing where the best powder will be.

Before we dive into natural terrain features that impact wind deposited snow, let's start simple with a manmade feature. A *snow fence* is used by the Colorado Department of Transportation to keep snow off roads (think Highway 93 between Boulder and Golden or Highway 285 near Fairplay)

---

the summer temperatures. Winds from year to year tend to remain somewhat constant overall. Ironically, winter-time snowfall has a lower correlation with the summer size of the snowfields than either spring-time snowfall or summer temperature.

and from loading avalanche paths that threaten highways (think Mt. Bethel just east of the Eisenhower Tunnel). How does a snow fence work? A snow fence slows down the wind, causing the snow to be deposited just beyond the snow fence. With less snow in the air beyond where it was deposited, the wind won't deposit as much snow where you don't want it (on the highway, in the starting zone of an avalanche path, etc.).[37] The snow fence effect is profound – a simple snow fence whether 4 feet high or 9 feet high, can deposit an incredible amount of snow in one location and keep it from being deposited in another location. And, snow fences aren't just used by the highway department. In Chapter 21, I'll discuss how ski areas use snow fences to capture snow where they want it.

But why is the snow being deposited just downwind of the snow fence? Because as a general matter wind picks up snow when the wind is accelerating and deposits snow when it is decelerating. A snow fence causes the wind to rapidly decelerate, thus forcing snow to be deposited just downwind of the snow fence.

Here is a helpful way to think about the concept, though it's only an analogy. Imagine you're on a bus heading home after a great day of skiing, and you are enjoying a nice cold beer in a glass. The bus is going at a steady 45 miles per hour. Your beer is not spilling. It's doing the equivalent of a steady wind. Then, suddenly, the bus driver slams on the brakes trying to slow to 10 miles per hour. You'll lurch forward and almost certainly spill the beer. Just as the beer goes all over the place when there's a rapid deceleration, similarly when wind transporting snow hits a snow fence, and perhaps drops from 45 miles per hour to 10 miles per hour almost instantly, the air lets go of the snow it is carrying. The snow fence is the brake, and the snow

---

[37] Unsurprisingly, much of the scientific research on the interplay between wind and snow has been done to either protect highways from snow deposits or to understand the impact of snow deposits on avalanche likelihood. Skiing wind deposited powder doesn't fund scientific studies, but road safety and avalanche safety does. Don't forget, we're learning how to find powder, but sadly the slopes where those powder stashes are located often carry greater avalanche risks.

is deposited like mad in the fast deceleration area just downwind of the snow fence.

Literally a four-foot-tall fence, something shorter than you, can drastically change snow patterns. This is both a scary and an exciting concept. It's scary because it greatly complicates searching out powder. But it's also exciting as it means even the smallest of changes in the shape of slopes can greatly increase the amount of powder you can ski. Okay, so far simple enough. If there's a snow fence, the deepest snow is just downwind of it.

Let's move to one step more complicated than a snow fence. Let's start with the effect of a simple ridge. (And we're talking about the geographical "ridge," not the upper air phenomenon.) Remember, snow is picked up from the ground by accelerating winds and deposited by decelerating winds. Wind tends to accelerate as it pushes up over the ridge. Why does it do this? Well, there are lots of factors involved, so let's keep this as simple as possible. At the simplest level, air close to the ground tends not to blow as fast (due to friction) as air higher up. In other words, let's say you are at a big cross-country ski area in flat terrain. If it's blowing at 5 miles per hour at your ankles, it may be blowing 10 miles per hour against your face, and 30 miles per hour 1,000 feet above you. But, if you go to that first ridge beyond the long flats just downwind of the cross-country ski area, and that ridge is 1,000 feet above the cross-country ski area, the winds will be much faster at the top of the ridge than at the cross-country ski area. The winds may not be a full 30 miles per hour due to the friction of the ridge, but they'll be much faster than they were at the cross-country ski area. Plus, as one ascends in elevation the air becomes less dense, so less force is necessary to make the air move faster. Simply, as you climb the ridge, the winds speed will increase, that is, the wind will accelerate. So, the wind is picking up snow as it ascends the ridge.

As soon as you're over the top, winds usually tend to slow down, i.e., to decelerate. The air has hit the brakes. The deceleration deposits snow, and I'll expand upon this in a minute. So, while orographic lifting may put more snow on the upwind (windward) side of the ridge, wind quickly more than makes up the difference by moving more snow to the downwind (leeward) side of the ridge. And, in fact more ski areas in Colorado are located on the downwind side of the mountain than the upwind side.

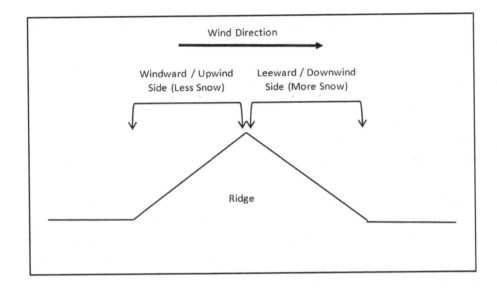

Let's move to one step more complicated than a simple ridge. (Don't worry, we won't get any more complicated than this step. And fortunately, we don't need to get any more complicated in order to understand the interplay between wind, powder, and terrain). Let's assume that instead of the ridge having the same angle on both sides, it rises gently on its western side (the upwind side) and drops off sharply on its eastern side (the downwind side).

What happens now? Well, you no doubt are familiar with the term *turbulence* (also called turbulent flow) from being bounced around on an airplane. The steep drop beyond the ridge creates turbulence. With the slope dropping off steeply beyond the ridge, the turbulent air can form an *eddy*. An eddy is a swirling flow of air (or any other "fluid" as scientists define fluids), in which part of that swirl goes in the reverse direction to the main flow. As you've doubtlessly seen in a fast-flowing stream, if a large rock blocks the flow, an eddy forms just below the rock where the water flows not downstream away from the rock but back uphill (i.e., upstream) towards the rock. Why does it do this? Because as the water is forced around the rock, it creates a void immediately below the rock that some water must fill by flowing back upstream.

The same thing occurs in the wind when air is transporting snow. As air flows over the steep ridge, the body of air creates a gap as the ridge rapidly drops out from under the air flow. This creates less pressure underneath the body of air, so the air rushes back in from below to fill the void. This means the wind at the surface of the snow is flowing in the opposite direction of the wind everywhere else. It is flowing back uphill. If the slope is not steep enough or the wind is not great enough, the wind just created what skiers happily call a *pillow*. With steeper slopes and/or more snow transport, this vertical eddy just created a *cornice*.

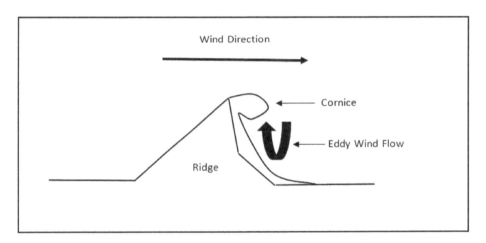

But pillows and cornices are only created when the air is moving fast enough. If it's not windy, the air does not become turbulent and eddies do not really form. Same thing is true for eddies in the creek – if the creek is flowing slowly, eddies do not form. If you want to geek out, the opposite of turbulent flow is called *laminar flow*, where the speed (and a few other technical inputs) mean that eddies will not form. This is the smooth flow you can feel with just a light wind – there are no gusts and lulls.

Oops. In the last paragraph I was getting awfully close to discussing Reynolds number, but I made a promise to you in the introduction that there will be no equations in this book. I am a man of my word, so let's stop the discussion before I throw out an equation. But, for those of you who are more scientifically inclined and not already familiar with Reynolds number, a quick online search of the equation will give you a better understanding of these issues.

Anyhow, laminar flow is easy for scientists to understand and predict. When turbulence occurs, however, chaos theory and the butterfly effect (see Chapter 12) once again rears its ugly head. As such, the butterfly effect throws true predictability of turbulence to the wind (no pun intended). Okay, we're again getting too deep into fluid dynamics, so let's step back and get simpler.

Let's talk about eddies for one more paragraph. While we typically thing of eddies playing out over a small area – for example, forming a 20-foot cornice – it often works on a much bigger or smaller scale. Here is an example from the summertime on a much larger scale. With friends in early August one time, I went to do a typical ski of Skyscraper Glacier north of Rollins Pass. We approached the glacier on the upwind (i.e., the windward / west) side of the continental divide ridge. There was a steady strong wind from the west – as one would expect. The wind disappeared the moment we descended to the east side of the ridge (i.e., downwind) a mere 20 feet to get onto the top of the glacier. After skiing the glacier, we removed our skis, and began the hike out. Not far from the bottom of the glacier, on the east side of Bob Lake, one of my friends noted that the winds had started back up, but it was now a light wind from the east. What was going on? The strong westerly wind went over the top of the ridge and a portion of that wind current rolled over until it was lightly blowing in the reverse direction, east, over Bob Lake and the lower portions of the glacier. This was a large eddy – we were already more than 600' vertical below the top of the ridge. No wonder Skyscraper Glacier accumulates so much snow.

Now we've already discussed wind speed in the context of turbulent versus laminar flow, but it's important to spend a bit more time on wind speed. The speed of the wind plays a major role in transport. As a rule of thumb (and yes, everything is a rule of thumb as it's always more complicated than this), if winds are less than roughly 10 miles an hour, the wind is insufficient to transport significant quantities of snow. Once the wind blows over 10 miles an hour or so, significant amounts of snow can be transported. (If you want to geek out on terminology, most snow is transported through a process called **saltation** – where snow bounces along the surface, not getting higher than roughly four inches above the surface.)

Things get interesting when the wind gets whipping. Above roughly 35 miles per hour, the wind suspends the snow in the air, which can be suspended as high as 300 feet above the ground. (The geeky term for this is **turbulent suspension**.) While blowing snow (i.e., turbulent suspension) is an attention grabber, it does not transfer nearly as much snow as saltation. The problem with turbulent suspension is that a significant portion of the snow suspended in the air can just sublimate (that is, turn into water vapor) and literally just disappear.

You may have heard the old skier joke in Colorado – that it's so windy today that all the snow is being blown to Kansas. The joke isn't really true. The snow is not being blown to Kansas. But it may still snow more in Kansas because of that crazy wind. Why? The fast wind, at turbulent suspension speeds, causes the snow to sublimate in the air, so it seemingly disappears. But it doesn't disappear – it just changes phase back to water vapor. As the air mass continues on to Kansas, there is now more water vapor in the air. So, the potential precipitation in Kansas is enhanced from what was blowing snow in Colorado.

WHERE TO SKI BASED ON THE WIND

Let's put this all together. If you want to ski deeper powder during or after windy times, where do you go? You want to go to where the wind is decelerating. Where is that? Where bushes, trees, snow fences, and most importantly, topography causes the wind to slow down. So, the lee (i.e., downwind) side of any feature will have better snow than the windward (i.e., upwind) side of any feature. This is perhaps demonstrated best in crossloading. My favorite example of this is anywhere you have north facing chutes. As you ski down those chutes, the better powder will be on the left side (i.e., the west side). Why? The sides of the couloir are mini-ridges, and with the prevailing winds from the west, the snow is pulled from the right side of the chute to your left and deposited onto the left side of the chute you are on. If you're skiing on the right side of your chute, there's less powder, because the wind is picking up that snow and depositing onto the next chute to your right.

What if you have an upslope storm (i.e., the storm sends the winds in from east to west)? Then the opposite happens – the skier's right side of north facing couloirs have better powder than the skier's left side of the same couloirs. Knowing where the wind is coming from and catching the terrain just downwind from terrain transitions makes for better skiing.

Further, there is a Goldilocks zone for wind speed in hunting powder. If the winds are too slow, they do not transport snow (and in any event there's no turbulence). At middle speeds, winds are great at transporting snow, and also the winds are moving fast enough to create turbulence, as the eddies and spirals of turbulence mean snow is decelerating and forming pillows. However, if the winds get going too fast, while some snow is transported, some of the snow also sublimates and goes to Kansas. Plus, it's not as much fun to ski when it's that windy.

Once you are already at a ski area, how can you find where the Goldilocks zone for powder will be based upon last night's winds? This brings us to the critical question of whether to ski above, below, or near treeline. *Treeline* is the elevation at which trees stop growing. Treeline in Colorado varies from a lowest elevation of almost 10,000' (in the Park Range north of Steamboat), to 10,800' (in certain portions of Rocky Mountain National Park and the Indian Peaks) to 12,000' (in various more southerly locations in the state). While many factors go into the elevation of treeline, the primary factor is summertime temperatures. This explains why treeline seems so low when skiing in the Alps and so high when skiing in Vermont. While skiing in the winter in Vermont seems much colder than Colorado – it's the warm summertime temperatures that define treeline. Likewise, for Coloradoans skiing in winter in the Alps, it seems like treeline should be much higher, but the summer in the Alps is far colder relative to Colorado.

Winds tend to be far greater above treeline than below treeline. There are, after all, no trees to decelerate the winds. Trees create friction, and without trees, there is less friction. This increase in winds above treeline is bolstered by the fact that an increase in elevation usually means an increase in winds. Because of this on many days, the winds have been just too high for there to be decent powder above treeline. However, on some days with only light winds, hunting for windblown powder is only possible above treeline – as the winds were too low below treeline to make any difference. In other words, it can be helpful to figure out where the Goldilocks zone on any particular day is for winds, so you can ski at the ideal elevation.

The same topographical rules apply above treeline for skiing as they do below treeline, and above treeline the rules are often magnified due to greater winds. So, minor depressions in the mountain can catch far more snow, and steep transitions create far larger cornices. Windward (i.e., up-wind) sides above treeline, especially close to the continental divide on the north end of the state, can often be completely stripped of snow for most of the winter. These areas that are stripped of snow (i.e., the areas that supply snow by wind to other areas) are called fetches.

For an example putting together much of what we've discussed, I took the picture on the next page in early season of a halfpipe in Colorado before any snowmaking or grooming occurred. This halfpipe faces northeast. Notice how the snow is plainly the deepest on the far looker's right (the northwest) side of the run. This shows both the cross-loading pattern, as well as the deceleration caused by the trees on the far right of the picture. The depression (formed by the halfpipe) has the second deepest snow in the picture, which also makes sense as it catches snow. Notice how the right side of the depression has more snow than the left side of the depression – again demonstrating the cross-loading. And, the least amount of snow is on the left side of the run just a little before the trees on the left side. Snow begins to reappear once back in the trees to the left side of the run.

A Couple of Caveats

With all of the foregoing information in mind, let's finish this chapter with two caveats – one on safety and the other one on snow quality. Naturally, we should start with safety.

A warning is in order. These above guidelines on finding wind transported powder are the same guidelines I teach in avalanche classes on places to avoid, because wind transported snow, pillows, and cornices are ripe spots for avalanches. So, on steeper slopes (i.e., roughly over thirty degrees – think

a black run pitch at most ski areas), particularly in the backcountry, be very wary of hunting powder by wind transport location as you are also hunting avalanche danger. (See Chapter 27.)

Finally, it's worth asking if wind-blown powder is as nice to ski as freshly fallen snow without wind? The answer is not really. If you'll notice, powder that has been blown into a location by the wind usually feels heavier. The reason why is surprisingly simple. Think about a beautiful snow crystal. When the wind picks it up and transports it, the wind breaks the outer more delicate branches of the crystal leaving just the inner parts. So, the snow crystals without their branches pack more densely than if they still had their branches. So, Colorado's famous cold smoke powder turns into a denser powder when blown about. And occasionally, it becomes so firm it's no longer really powder.

But, if given the choice to ski 2 inches of perfect blower powder, or 12 inches of denser wind transported powder, I'll go for the 12 inches of heavier powder. Every time.

Chapter 20

Powder From the Ground Up: Recycled Powder Explained

P owder snow comes only from the sky. False.

Large beautiful snow crystals can form in clouds and fall down from the sky as fresh powder. Or, large beautiful snow crystals can form in the snowpack already on the ground. And then, the snowpack has grown itself fresh powder for you to ski. What is this mythical beast that allows powder to form days after the storm?

It's called recycled powder. In order to increase your odds of finding recycled powder, it helps to understand how it is formed.

In Chapter 7 we discussed how snow crystals form in clouds. But frankly it's a little more important to understand how beautiful snow crystals form in the snowpack than in clouds. Why? It's the exact same process that creates recycled powder that creates one of the most dangerous layers from an avalanche perspective – facets. So, pay attention, this matters.

And unlike snow crystal formation in the clouds, which remains shrouded in mystery, we actually have a pretty good idea of snow crystal formation in the snowpack. This is because it's a heck of a lot easier to observe. While teaching avalanche classes and/or making avalanche observations, it's easy for me to take out my microscope and look at ice crystals in various stages of development while standing in a snowpit. It's all happening at ground level and in the same place. If only studying microscopic changes in clouds was so easy!

Let's start with the big picture to explain recycled powder. Once snow has fallen onto the ground – it will slowly change and go through metamorphosis until it eventually melts – often six or nine months later. We'll discuss this science here, but if you're not the science type, don't worry. If you can understand beer, you can understand snow science.

Question, if you have to leave a six-pack of beer overnight in the Colorado mountains, are you best leaving it on the surface of the snow, burying it half-way down in the snowpack, or burying it all the way at the bottom, against the ground itself? Think about this before reading the next sentence. The answer is the third choice. If you leave it on the surface, the night temperatures in Colorado will surely freeze and destroy the beer. If you bury it halfway down the snowpack, it will be far colder than freezing, and once again, the beer will likely freeze. The ground however is for all intents and purposes always 32 degrees Fahrenheit (0 Celsius) in Colorado. So, your beer will not freeze overnight, and boy will it taste nice and refreshing come morning.

Where to bury a beer in the snowpack is key because if there's a large temperature gradient (i.e., a large temperature difference between the cold nighttime surface of the snow and the warmer ground) *facets* form. If there is not a large temperature gradient, *rounds* form. And this is important because facets at the surface are also known as *recycled powder*. I'll use the term facets for the rest of the chapter, as to understand facets and faceting, we need to talk about more than just facets on the surface (i.e., recycled powder).

Facets are large crystals that don't bond together well – you can't make snowballs out of them as they'd just fall apart. They're often called sugar snow, and that's how they feel. It's like skiing through soft sugar. Rounds, on the other hand, would make far better snowballs if they weren't so darn cold. Rounds are a lot more solid. They bond together to form strong layers. People often get confused as there are countless names for these two types of snow,[38] but it's fair just to call them facets and rounds, remembering that facets on the surface is the glorious recycled powder.

---

[38] There are many synonyms for facets and rounds. As such, the terminology can be confusing, especially when reading older avalanche books. Here is a chart that shows all the common (and most of the historical) names for facets and for rounds:

Below is a photograph of facets on my ski glove. If you tried to make a snowball out of this stuff, you'd look pretty silly.

Facets (other names)	Rounds (other names)
Recycled Powder (when on the top of the snowpack)	ET Snow
Depth Hoar (when on the bottom of the snowpack)	Equi-temperature snow
Persistent Snow	Strong snow
Squares	Equilibrium metamorphism
Sugar Snow	Destructive metamorphism snow
Weak Snow	
Temperature Gradient Snow	
TG Snow	
Kinetic metamorphism snow	
Constructive metamorphism snow	

Facets form if there is greater than a 1 degree Centigrade difference over 10 cm of snow (i.e., 2 degrees Fahrenheit change over 4 inches).[39] So, to take a simple (arguably oversimple) example, if the snowpack is 1 meter deep (just over 3 feet) and the nighttime temperature is -8 degrees Centigrade (18 degrees Fahrenheit), rounds will form as there's less than a 1 degree Centigrade change per 10 cm. (Remember, the ground, where you bury the beer is always 0 degrees Centigrade, i.e., 32 degrees Fahrenheit.) And yes, I'm sorry I'm actually making you do arithmetic. But look on the bright side, when I do this arithmetic myself, I can often do it on my fingers without having to take off my shoes to count toes.

However, if the snowpack is only 0.5 meters deep (20 inches) in the same conditions, facets will form as there is greater than a 1 degree Centigrade change for every 10 cm. In other words, if you have the exact same temperatures and if the snowpack is a mid-November snowpack that is 20 inches deep, you get facets. If it's a mid-December snowpack that is 40 inches deep, you get rounds. What does this mean? Cold nights or a shallow snowpack means more facets. Warmer nights or a deeper snowpack means more rounds. Faceting is often more common early in the season with a shallow snowpack – but when temperatures dip to very cold at night in February, it's not uncommon to see faceting then as well.

Now from a technical standpoint, it's not the temperature gradient but the water vapor gradient that causes the formation of facets. As temperatures are much easier to measure and think about (I bet you've commented about the cold or heat recently, but I doubt you've commented about the vapor pressure recently), we use temperature as the shorthand method of discussing this issue. Nevertheless, here's what's really going on in the snow. Warm air holds more moisture than cold air. (Indeed, that's why it snows. When a cloud rises and gets colder, it can no longer hold as much moisture and must precipitate it out in the form of snow.) So, wherever its warmer in the snowpack (for example, the ground), in the spaces between the snow crystals there is a greater vapor pressure. And near the surface there is less vapor pressure.

---

[39] Okay, this is one of the few times I prefer metric units (other than millibars) to freedom units, but this is an exception. (See my footnote rant in Chapter 7.)

The vapor moves from areas of higher concentration to lower concentration, so the water vapor moves up the snowpack, and converts straight from gas to solid, depositing on the bottom of the snow crystal above it. It deposits onto this crystal in a linear fashion, locking into place, which creates long striated feathery crystals. These large crystals on the surface are amazing to ski.

Now, this whole process can only work if the snow is porous enough for there to be sufficient water vapor within the snowpack to grow the snow crystals. If the snow is packed too tightly, it cannot facet. This is why you'll never find enough recycled powder on a groomed ski run or a bump run. There have just been too many skiers skiing the run, compacting the snow. But, deeper into the trees at ski areas, and throughout the backcountry, recycled powder is a wonderful and not unusual find.[40]

PUTTING IT ALL TOGETHER

What have we learned? In places that do not see heavy skier compaction – cold nights produce recycled powder. Likewise, a shallow snowpack is more likely to produce recycled powder (which is ironic because who would think that less total snow on the ground produces better powder). So, if it hasn't snowed for a while, and if it's been cold enough, the low skier traffic locations will get recycled powder.

In my life, I've skied recycled powder many times in the backcountry at roughly half a foot deep. Only once in my life have I found thigh-deep

---

[40]   The arguably ultimate type of recycled powder to ski has a terrifyingly complicated sounding scientific name. But don't let the name scare you – there's nothing better than skiing recycled powder from *diurnal recrystallization*. Diurnal just means variations between day and night. And recrystallization just means creating new crystals (here snow crystals). So the scary sounding name is just the day/night temperature swing causing snow crystal growth. And big snow crystals equal awesome powder. Diurnal recrystallization is the result of large daytime/nighttime temperature swings, that actually cause the faceted snow crystals to grow in size both downward from water vapor moving upward and depositing on the crystal above it (at night), and upward from the water vapor moving downwards and depositing on the crystal below it (during the day).

recycled powder on a steep slope. I was skiing near High Trail Cliffs north of Berthoud Pass. With all the powder I've skied in my life, to remember any one run anymore is nearly impossible. But I will never forget the sensation of skiing through this magnificent thigh-deep recycled powder – a pool of bottomless facets on a steep slope. I can only hope to live long enough and be in the perfect spot again to experience such snow once again at such depth.

Recycled powder is awesome. Just remember the dark side of it when it gets buried under more snow, as we'll discuss in Chapter 27 on avalanches.

Chapter 21

Human Created Snow – From Snow Guns to Cloud Seeding

While nature makes the best snow, technology has gotten to the point where we can lend mother nature a hand now and again, whether through manmade snow, grooming, snow fences, or cloud seeding. Let's quickly explore these options of man creating, or helping to create, more snow. But fair warning – the first two methods don't provide for powder snow.

MANMADE SNOW

While it's not powder, understanding snowmaking is helpful for dedicated skiers. Let's first discuss exactly what manmade snow is, then we'll discuss when ski areas can make snow, and finally let's discuss the extent of snow-making operations in Colorado.

Manmade snow, from a technical standpoint, isn't really snow. Rather, it is technically sleet. Snow is formed by water vapor freezing / condensing. Put another way, a snowflake is largely the result of water vapor converting directly into ice. Sleet, on the other hand, is formed by water droplets freezing. Manmade snow is the latter – frozen water droplets. In order to make "snow," water is combined with compressed air and typically a nucleating agent.[41] It is then shot out of a snowmaking machine. Snowmaking

---

[41] Do you remember in Chapter 7, how snow crystals do not form without specks of dust on which to freeze? The same is true for snowmaking. To assist

machines typically come in two types – either a fan (also known as a low pressure jet) or a gun (also known as a high pressure jet). The latter can be either a tower gun or a ground gun. The advantage of a fan is that it is more efficient, but each fan unit requires its own power source, which requires a more expensive infrastructure.

Regardless of whether the water droplets are shot out of a fan or gun, the water droplets freeze around the nucleating agent as they go through the air. They freeze before they hit the ground. Then, the frozen water falls onto the ski slope. This is, technically, basically sleet.

Of course, imagine that you work for a snowmaking company. Would you want to tell people you work for a sleetmaking company as opposed to a snowmaking company? Of course not. And how do you sell your coolest and most innovative new sleet gun to ski areas? You can't. It just doesn't sound sexy. You want to sell a snow gun as the word "snow" just sounds so much better than "sleet." And the same thing is true for the guests. After all, who wants to hear a ski area say that they've been blasting their sleet guns for 36 hours straight, and they plan to open for the season on Friday with an 18" base of manmade sleet.

Now, this is not meant to speak ill of manmade sleet (uh, I mean manmade snow). You should be thankful for manmade snow. For some purposes like building a base, it is far better than real snow. Manmade snow creates an incredible base at the beginning of the ski season precisely because it is

---

in freezing, nucleating agents are often added. Ironically, one of the popular nucleating agents for snowmaking is a bacteria, *psedomonas syringae*, which naturally developed a skill for creating ice at relatively warm temperatures that has nothing to do with snowmaking. Rather, the bacteria is a plant pathogen, and so it would create ice to encourage frost damage to its victim plants to make them more susceptible to bacterial infection. Out of this awful purpose, this bacteria has become quite useful and benign in creating snow at higher temperatures.

This isn't the only ingredient that is often added to water before making snow. Another product often used changes the shape of the water droplets to be more elongated. With a greater surface area ratio to mass from the elongation, the water droplets freeze easier.

technically sleet and not snow. The higher water content creates a strong stable base-layer that would otherwise require copious amounts of natural snow. Yeah sleet!

There's no great powder skiing on freshly made manmade snow. (Trust me, as a ski patroller I've had the opportunity to ski the snowmaking whales right after snowmaking is done and before the groomers push the whales of snow onto a uniform surface. It doesn't ski anything like powder.) Manmade snow varies from 18% to 50% water content, depending upon the environment and inputs.[42]

Colorado's winter-time storms tend to be 8% or less water content, which is why our snow is famous around the world for being so light. Colorado's heavy spring-time storms are often around 10-12% water content. But when you compare 18-50% water content from snowmaking to 6-12% water content in snowstorms, it makes sense that there's no snowmaking powder. But this high water content also makes it clear why snowmaking is so good for building a base. Indeed, a run after it has been extensively groomed has a water content of approximately 50% – not that much higher than the water content from snowmaking. Without snowmaking it may be difficult early season to open a resort (even with powder at the higher elevations) without snowmaking at the lower elevations.

Contrary to what many people believe, the question of whether it's cold enough or not for a ski area to make snow is not based upon air temperature. Rather, it is based upon the combination of air temperature and humidity. Why is this? It's due to ***evaporative cooling***.

---

[42] As a reminder, water content is the ratio of snow to water. If you simply measure the volume of snow, and then melt it and measure the volume of water it produces, the ratio of water to snow is the water content.

Depending upon the source, some claim the average water content of snowmaking snow is 25% and others claim the average water content of snowmaking snow is 40%. Nevertheless, comparing the range of water content from snowmaking versus the range of water content from natural snow demonstrates the drastic difference, regardless of the actual average water content of snowmaking snow.

When you sweat, your body cools down because it takes energy for the water on your skin (i.e., your sweat) to evaporate. To get that energy to evaporate, the water must pull the energy from somewhere. It pulls the energy from your skin, so your skin cools as the water evaporates. At higher humidity, less water evaporates so the cooling effect is reduced. That's why taking a jog in the morning at 75 degrees in Colorado is usually pretty pleasant as we live in a dry climate, while taking the same jog in the morning at 75 degrees in Georgia is usually pretty miserable as Georgia is a humid climate. Your body's cooling system is a lot more effective with low humidity.

The water droplets leaving the snow gun are going through the exact same process as your body. In drier conditions, there is greater evaporation that cools the remaining portion of the water droplet and its immediate vicinity. As such, the air temperature does not even need to be below freezing for the water droplets to freeze.

From a technical standpoint, the effects of evaporative cooling would let one make snow at roughly 43 degrees Fahrenheit if the relative humidity is 0%.[43] Relative humidity is never 0%, not even in the Sahara Desert, but you get the idea. If relative humidity is 20%, technically you can make snow up to roughly 37 degrees. But if relative humidity is 70%, you cannot make

---

[43] This entire discussion involves the standard type of snowmaking in Colorado using either tower or ground guns (i.e., high pressure jet) or fans (i.e., low pressure jet). However, there are other methods of making snow, which can be done at virtually any temperature.

   The refrigeration method of making snow is pretty cool. Snow is made in a refrigerated tractor trailer sized internal unit and is then blown out onto the mountain at any outside air temperature. Due to the cost of the system, its comparative energy inefficiency, and the fear of using too much water that will just melt – this refrigeration method of snowmaking is rarely used in the Rocky Mountains.

   How great would it be, however, if someday technological advances permit widespread application of this method? If so, in competing to open first, ski areas in the fall would only be looking at the melt rate of the snow on the ground, not the temperature at which to make snow. My fingers are crossed for this to happen, but I'm not holding my breath.

snow unless the temperature is less than roughly 29 degrees. Anyone caught the irony in this yet? It's much easier to make snow when it's dry than when it's snowing.

The shorthand way to determine whether one can make snow is based upon the wet bulb temperature.[44] If the wet bulb temperature is below 28 degrees Fahrenheit (-2 Celsius), one can technically make snow. People religiously watch the CAIC's WRF model's forecasts for wet bulb temperature at each ski area that starts making snow in October, to see when snowmaking will be possible.

Now, the 28 degrees wet bulb temperature is the maximum temperature that a ski area can make snow. The ski area doesn't actually want to make snow so close to the line. It's pretty inefficient. And, minor changes in temperature or humidity when this close to the line could mean you start blowing water as opposed to snow. That would obviously be a bad thing. Snowmakers fear the rainbow — when one can see a rainbow in the plume of snow from the gun. That is a bad sign. It means that not all the water is freezing.

So, in reality, what is the temperature snowmakers look for in order to efficiently make snow? The answer is a wet bulb temperature of 18 degrees or less. When the wet bulb temperature falls below 18 degrees, it's game on for efficient snowmaking.

When nights start to become colder and drier in the fall, snowmaking starts. This is why ski areas like A-Basin, Keystone, and Loveland can start making snow in late-September — all you need are nights where the temperature dips below freezing, and conditions are dry. Of course, the colder / drier it gets, the more efficient snowmaking becomes. And, ground temperatures at freezing as opposed to above freezing certainly helps the snowmaking process to get terrain open, as does snow from mother nature.

---

[44] The wet-bulb temperature is the temperature measured by a thermometer covered in a wet ski sock and swung around through the air. I'm not making that up. In short, the wet bulb temperature takes into account evaporative cooling and reads at a lower temperature than a normal thermometer due to evaporative cooling.

So, making snow in late November can open terrain at a much quicker pace than making snow in early October.

Most but not all ski areas in Colorado have snowmaking. Those without snowmaking brag (and rightfully so) that their snow is 100% natural, and that leads to a softer base (which it does). And, having no snowmaking can save a ski resort a ton of money in costs. Making snow is basically blowing cash out of a snow gun and onto the mountainside. The resorts without any snowmaking include Hesperus, Kendall, Monarch, Silverton, and Ski Cooper.

But having zero snowmaking is not typical in Colorado, and most resorts want some snowmaking. Of those resorts that do have snowmaking, some have it only on a few key runs to make sure that they can either open early, open regardless of snowfall, or make sure a well-traveled route holds enough snow to stay open even if the areas around it can get by just on natural snow. The ski areas with 10% or less total snowmaking coverage include Arapahoe Basin, Powderhorn, Snowmass, Sunlight, Vail, and Wolf Creek. In fact, Wolf Creek's snowmaking only covers 5 acres of the 1600 acres of total terrain at the resort.

Many Colorado ski areas have far more extensive snowmaking networks, some covering many dozens of trails. Only a handful, however, make snow on more than half their runs. And only one ski area, Howelsen Hill, has 100% snowmaking coverage. When put all together, roughly 12% of the total ski area terrain in Colorado has snowmaking on it.

In sum, manmade snow is not powder. But it does allow us to ski earlier in the season, it allows us to have a reliable base in bad snow years. And, it allows us to access the more crowded and low elevation terrain. So, snow-making is a pretty great thing.

SNOW GROOMING

While snow grooming does not create powder, grooming machines can transport large quantities of snow. This makes a difference where on the mountain one can find snow. Look at any large terrain park, and the quantity of snow moved by ski areas becomes readily apparent. Grooming machines work hard not only to make quality groomer runs as discussed in Chapter 32, but also to get snow where it's wanted.

How do they do this? Next time you look at a grooming machine (also known as a snowcat), notice how there are three parts to it. There is a front attachment, the machine itself, and the rear attachment. The front attachment is usually a blade, but it can also be a bucket or a snow blower. The primary purpose of the bucket and/or snow blower is to move snow. The blade likewise does a great job of moving snow (though it also does double duty in preparing the slope to be groomed).

Moving snow around is important. When mother nature doesn't provide sufficient snow in popular ski paths, especially at lower elevations, as long as there is enough snow elsewhere on the mountain that is accessible by snowcat, snow can be pushed, carried, or blown into the areas that need snow. Similarly, the loading areas of lifts frequently need more snow, so groomers push snow into these areas as well.

Perhaps the most interesting groomer transport of snow for those reading this book is late season work. Back in the 1990s when I worked at Berthoud Pass, for a couple of years we tried to compete with A-Basin to be the last ski area open in Colorado. While we never won the race to be the last open – we were able to compete by pushing snow from one location to another. As the south facing runs would start to melt out – we would close groomer accessible south facing runs and have the grooming machine push the snow from these recently closed runs to the open runs that we thought we could keep open longer. We continued this process as we continued to close runs that the groomer could access. We'd keep moving the remaining snow to the runs we thought we could keep open the longest. And importantly, we also had to manage run-off water. Cutting channels and routes for water to run-off without damaging the remaining snow was key to maintaining our remaining snowpack.

Simply, grooming work transports snow, if not powder. So, it's worth knowing about.

SNOW FENCES

As discussed in more depth in Chapter 19, snow on the ground is picked up in accelerating wind and is deposited in decelerating winds. So, let's say you work at a ski area and windstorms are blowing snow off the headwall of one of your great runs into the trees beyond your boundary. What do you do? There is a simple and cost-effective solution. Put up snow fences.

Snow fences cause wind to decelerate downwind of the snow fence. And what happens when wind is decelerating? It deposits the snow it is transporting. So, by putting snow fences on ski runs perpendicular to the typical winds, it means that more snow will end up on the ski run. As ski runs tend to be pretty snowy already, the resulting snow captured from these snow fences may not be as easy to see as the highway version of snow fences. If you drive during the winter on any of the highways with snow fences, such as Highway 93 between Boulder and Golden or Highway 285 near Fairplay, you will see the extensive snow deposits downwind of the snow fence. The same thing occurs at the ski area, though you may not notice it unless you use the snow fence as a guide of where to find the deepest powder.

There's an art in determining where to place snow fences. Snow fences that are not generally perpendicular to the main wind direction do not do much good. If a snow fence is placed too far upwind on the run, you may be stealing snow from the far downwind side of the run. Similarly, if a snow fence is placed too far downwind on a run, it may not capture enough snow to be worthwhile. Fortunately, ski areas tend to learn from experience with their local topography where the best spots are to place snow fences.

Many ski areas use snow fences only early season before runs open to the public to help build the snow base. Other ski areas use portable snow fences throughout the season to get wind transported snow to be deposited in the right spots and not the wrong spots. These portable snow fences are particularly helpful as they can be dug out after big storms and placed higher in the growing snowpack. And, a few ski areas have permanently placed snow fences to keep snow in the best spots all winter long. For enjoying powder, the portable snow fences that are used throughout the season are the best ones.

If you want to increase the depth of the snow you're skiing, look for snow fences. Skiing just a bit downwind of each one will provide deeper powder than in locations without the snow fences.

CLOUD SEEDING

Here's some trivia. Just like chemical warfare is banned by UN Convention, weather warfare is banned by UN Convention. What is weather warfare, you may ask?

During the Vietnam War, the U.S. Military sought to prolong the monsoon season to keep the Ho Chi Minh Trail muddy. The best method it found was cloud seeding, which rings out more precipitation from clouds. The cloud seeding operation seemed to have some success, but its use led to a nearly world-wide ban, put in place in 1978, of weather warfare.

This begs the question, what exactly is cloud seeding?

In the 1940s, American scientists discovered almost by accident that adding minute quantities of dry ice to an artificial cloud kept in a laboratory freezer would cause the cloud to produce precipitation. They quickly learned that silver iodide was even more effective than dry ice. Out of these experiments, the idea of cloud seeding was born.

If you'll recall from Chapter 7, in order for a snow crystal to form, it must freeze around a speck of dust with the right chemical properties. It turns out that silver iodide has the perfect chemical arrangement to serve as a *freezing nuclei* – the speck of dust on which the snow crystal begins its formation.

Cloud seeding cannot make a cloud. But, when there's already a cloud, providing a plentiful quantity of freezing nuclei should, in theory, coax more snow out of the cloud.

Multiple Colorado ski areas pay the high price of cloud seeding to try to get a bit more snow out of a storm. I remember once riding a chairlift with a friend of mine in the ski industry, and when discussing how several more inches of snow fell at his resort than predicted by Open Snow, he commented that they paid a lot of money to get those extra several inches.

The effectiveness of cloud seeding, however, is mired in controversy. In order to measure the effectiveness of cloud seeding, you would have to know how much it would have snowed without the cloud seeding. As I've repeatedly discussed in the book, that's a nearly impossible task to solve as forecasted snowfall is simply not predictive enough to make sure the comparison is proper. The findings and conclusions from the studies that have looked at cloud seeding are all over the map. Some find no statistically significant increase in snowfall, while others find that cloud seeding may well increase snowfall by 10 percent or more. Regardless of its exact effectiveness, a number of ski areas have cloud seeding programs. Assuming it actually works, we skiers do appreciate it.

PART 6

CLIMATOLOGY AND HUNTING
POWDER

"Climate is what you expect, weather is what you get" famously and accurately remarked writer Robert A. Heinlein. A location's climate is what the location normally sees as weather. Put another way, it is the average weather at a location. So, if we're talking about the likelihood of snow two weeks out, it's more helpful to talk about climate – that is what the typical weather patterns are – than to talk about what long range weather models may or may not be predicting.

So, let's explore several of these climate questions. If you're only looking at climate – which is what most out-of-state visitors must do when booking a trip to Colorado – what can you expect typical snow conditions to look like in Colorado's different regions? From a timing perspective, what are the seasons like in terms of skiing in Colorado? Which months are better than other months by region within Colorado? When can you make the switch from considering climate to weather?

And of course, I thought it would only make sense to share with you the many tricks and tips I have for hunting powder at ski areas, when the snow does arrive.

Chapter 22

Understanding Colorado's Snow Regions

The most reliable predictor of snow conditions more than a week and a half or so away is not the weather forecast, but climate averages. And even when your ski day is within a real forecast range, understanding a location's climate is still critical to understanding what the predicted snowfall will really mean for you when you're skiing.

While on a map Colorado looks like a big rectangle, only the western two-thirds of the state contain its mountains. And these mountains and their snow are hardly uniform. I think typical Colorado snow conditions are best viewed as dividing the mountain portions of the state into four different regions. To be clear, dividing the state into these four conceptual regions does not mean that they all get snow from similar wind patterns or storm paths. They do not. Elevation, mountain topography, and latitude all play into the mix. But to generalize based upon snow quality, best months, and relative winds, here you go.

First, there is the *Classic Colorado* region of the state – lots of snow, lots of sun, and comparatively moderate winds. This region extends from the western San Juan Mountains (Silverton and Telluride) in the southwest corner of the state, through the Elk Mountains (Aspen, Crested Butte, and Snowmass), through the Sawatch / Gore Mountains (Beaver Creek and Vail) in the center of the state, to the Elkhead / Park Mountains (Steamboat) in the northern part of the state. While different storm tracks hit these areas within the Classic Colorado region in different ways, the average snow quality and overall snow patterns within this region are similar.

On average, this area gets its best snow in the winter months. And, as a general matter, winds from the west are the best snow producers for these areas, though a few mountains like Telluride seem to pick up as much or more snow with winds from the southwest. Winds from the northwest aren't bad for this region either.

This region tends to average less than 8% water content in its snow. This places it among the lightest snow anywhere in the world with good mountains for skiing. Hooray for Colorado!

Two of the three snowiest spots in the state are located in this region, though ironically there are no ski areas located in either of these spots. These locations are the northern Park Range (north of Steamboat), and the west Elks (west of Crested Butte / Snowmass).

Second, while it can certainly be windy in the Classic Colorado portion of Colorado, as one gets closer to the continental divide in the northern two-thirds of the state, winds tend to increase. Fortunately, neither the amount of snow nor the number of sunny days decreases. For lack of a better term, I'll refer to this region as the **Continental Divide** region.[45]

The continental divide areas tend to get big snow both in the winter and springtime. Although an overgeneralization, northwest and west winds are the best wind directions for these areas. And, as they are within the spillover effect area for upslope storms, they pick up decent snow when the winds are coming from the east and southeast.

Like Classic Colorado, the Continental Divide region averages less than 8% water content in freshly fallen snow. In other words, although windier,

---

[45] For those unfamiliar with the term continental divide, it is simply the line running (very roughly) from north to south through the Rocky Mountains, which divides the watersheds of the Atlantic and Pacific Ocean. So, if you are standing at the top of Chair 9 at Loveland, which is at the top of the continental divide, and you spit to the west, your spit will end up in the Pacific Ocean. And, if you spit to the east, your spit will end up in the Atlantic Ocean. As an aside, I'd really rather you not do that. I'd hate for Loveland to call me up and complain that because of this book everyone is spitting at the top of Chair 9.

the snow is almost as fluffy near the continental divide as it is in Classic Colorado.

The precise location of this Continental Divide region is a bit fuzzy as the weather gods don't care about hydrology. Put another way, the continental divide is technically the demarcation between whether the water flows to the Atlantic Ocean or the Pacific Ocean. As such, the continental divide is a high dividing line – but many other high and lengthy terrain in Colorado creates its own pseudo-continental divide weather patterns. The Ten Mile Range, for example, acts somewhat like the continental divide. So, Breckenridge, which is high in the Ten Mile Range, shares many weather similarities with Loveland, which is on the continental divide itself, even though Breckenridge is roughly a dozen miles from the actual continental divide.

And, this doesn't count the southern parts of the state where the continental divide jogs far westward. Wolf Creek Pass is technically on the continental divide, but it by no means shares the features we're discussing here when we speak of continental divide snow.

Regardless of its precise location, the Continental Divide region extends to a couple miles to the east of the Continental Divide (but still within the spillover effect, a key concept discussed in Chapter 2). Loveland and Monarch Mountain, both technically just east of the Continental Divide, are really in this region as they are within the spillover effect from storms coming from the western half of the compass.

Third, there are the areas truly to the ***East of the Continental Divide*** – think Pikes Peak or Bear Lake (in Rocky Mountain National Park). Again, for this definition, let's ignore the far southern reaches of the state. Once one gets beyond the spillover effect just east of the Continental Divide, the average winter snowfall decreases somewhat, and the average wind speed increases drastically. When teaching the weather portions of avalanche classes, I often refer to this region as the Vermont of Colorado – colder, windier, and less snow than the rest of Colorado – but like Vermont, still containing plenty of good skiing and many quality powder days. It's a good description in teaching a class as it's easy to remember, but at best it's an oversimplification both of this region and of Vermont.

Unlike the Classic Colorado locations, the East of the Continental Divide region tends to see its biggest snowfall totals in the fall, and especially in the springtime, as opposed to during the winter. How big can these East of the Continental Divide Region snowstorms get? Well, the United States record for the most snow in 24 hours was not set on some volcano in Washington or mountain in Alaska. Rather, it was set in this region from a mid–April storm a century ago – a whopping 76 inches of snow in 24 hours.

The best wind directions for snow for this region tend to be from the east and southeast. See Chapters 3 and 4 for a description of why winds from the eastern half of the compass are the best winds for this region.

Finally, the fourth region of Colorado is the smallest area geographically, though its snow patterns are so unique, it warrants its own description. The *Wolf Creek Pass* region, or the eastern San Juan Mountains, get more snow on average, and denser snow on average, than any other part of Colorado. Just like I refer to the areas to the East of the Continental Divide as the Vermont of Colorado, I often colloquially refer to Wolf Creek Pass area of Colorado as the Utah of Colorado. Utah (specifically the Cottonwood Canyons) on average, gets both more snow and heavier snow than Colorado, and the snow in the Wolf Creek Pass area often seems far more analogous to Utah snow than Colorado snow. It may seem odd that Red Mountain Pass (halfway between Telluride and Silverton), which is 50 miles closer to the Pacific Ocean than Wolf Creek Pass, has much lighter snow. Nevertheless, Red Mountain Pass's average water content is less than 8%, while Wolf Creek Pass's average water content is over 10%.[46]

---

[46] So how much denser is Utah's snow on average than Colorado's snow? Hold on as I'm about to go down a rabbit hole, but I do love rabbit holes.

Avalanche literature places Colorado and New Mexico in the continental snowpack category, which averages roughly 7% water content. Utah, Idaho, Wyoming, and Montana are in the intermountain snowpack category with roughly 9% water content. And California, Oregon, and Washington are in the maritime snowpack category with roughly 12% water content. But like all data, this is derived from one study (Armstrong and Armstrong 1987) and not all studies agree.

A fascinating earlier study (LaChappelle 1962) compared snow at Berthoud Pass, Colorado with Alta, Utah and a number of other locations in other states.

Don't let Wolf Creek Pass's higher water content put you off – sometimes slightly heavier snow is as much fun, if not more fun, to ski. And, as an added bonus, denser snow tends to cling onto steeper terrain than less dense snow. Wolf Creek Ski Area's Knife Ridge is "exhibit A" for this principle.

So why are Red Mountain Pass and Wolf Creek Pass so different when it comes to snow? Southwesterly flow that hammers Wolf Creek doesn't hit Red Mountain Pass with the same force. And, storms from the southwest tend to be warmer (as they're coming from the warmer parts of the Pacific Ocean), so they produce heavier snow. Southwest storms are the greatest gift to Wolf Creek. In fact, during Wolf Creek's best ski season on record, it picked up a nearly unfathomable 838 inches of snow in one year. That's nearly 70 feet!

I should note that Wolf Creek Ski Area and Wolf Creek Pass get snow from more directions than just the southwest. After all, you don't get the award of being Colorado's snowiest accessible spot without picking snow up from winds in many directions. So, Wolf Creek gets good snowfall from many directions beyond just from the southwest. But wind from the southwest are certainly the best direction for Wolf Creek.

In this study, the mean water content of snow at Berthoud Pass was 6.9% and the median was 7%, while the mean water content at Alta was 10% and the median was 9%. (There's a nice chart showing the distribution of water content of storms by location in the Nolan Doesken book listed in Appendix F.)

Relying upon yet two further and more recent studies, Jim Steenburgh's Greatest Snow on Earth book puts Alta at an average of 8.4% compared to 7.2% at Steamboat Springs, 7.6% at the Eisenhower Tunnel, and 7.5% at Red Mountain Pass. Fascinatingly, Wolf Creek Pass falls at 10.3%.

So, what can we say overall? While the Cottonwood Canyons of Utah (and Wolf Creek) have blower powder days, these days are less common than the blower powder days in the rest of Colorado. On average, Utah (and Wolf Creek) see heavier snow than the rest of Colorado – though exactly how much heavier is not completely clear. From my personal experience of skiing lots of backcountry powder in both the Cottonwood Canyons and the Berthoud Pass region, Berthoud Pass on average has significantly lighter powder, but the Cottonwood Canyons get more snow.

Okay, let's climb back out of the rabbit hole now, but I do love rabbit holes.

My favorite story about how much snow falls at Wolf Creek comes from a random conversation I had with a hotel owner in South Fork, Colorado, near Wolf Creek a few years ago. It was one of those extraordinary snow years in Colorado, and as usual Wolf Creek had received the most snow up to that point in the state. I asked him how the winter had been so far for him, saying that I assumed it was terrific. "No," he responded, "it's been kind of a bad year business-wise." I was perplexed. I asked him how this was possible, and he responded – "every year is a great snow year at Wolf Creek. More people stay at my hotel when there's bad snow everywhere else." It was unintentionally the highest praise one could give to how great a snow region it is.

If you want more information on snow patterns in any of these four regions, check out Appendix A, which provides resort by resort information.

Chapter 23

When to Hunt Powder (Part One) – a Guide to All Four Seasons

If you are trying to schedule a trip to Colorado to go skiing, what's the best month? Or, if you already live in Colorado, what's the best month to take time off from work to ski more?

Colorado ski resorts provide skiing for almost nine months out of the year. Backcountry skiers can ski every month of the year in Colorado. I ski every month of the year in Colorado, and the only month I have never skied fresh powder in Colorado is the month of August. So, any complete guide on hunting powder must address all four seasons. Let's start with the fall.

THE FALL

For the past decade, every year A-Basin and Loveland take out their snow making equipment in September, fire the snow guns up as soon as it gets cold enough (see Chapter 21), and race each other to be the first resort open. And, starting in 2019, Keystone has joined the race. (I should say re-joined the race because back in the 1990s and early 2000s before A-Basin installed a snowmaking system, Keystone and Loveland would compete to be the first ski area open.)

Typically, A-Basin and Loveland open in mid-October, starting with one lift and one route down the mountain. In the last couple of decades, the earliest opening date for any ski area in Colorado was October 7, 2009 and the latest opening date for the first ski area to open in Colorado was October 29, 2015. For those who are overly curious, Appendix D has the opening day of the first ski area open each ski season since the mid-1990s. Soon after these ski areas open with one route down the mountain, they begin opening more new terrain as weather allows.

While the opening competition between the ski areas is awesome, don't bet on powder when there are two or three ski areas open and only a handful of open runs. Once and a while, however, a large early season snowfall somewhere else in the state permits another ski resort to open on natural snow before either A-Basin, Keystone, or Loveland.

Wolf Creek has the occasional years when it has beaten the other resorts to be the first one open. Usually this is when an early snow hits the San Juan Mountains, and when Wolf Creek opens early season after a storm, it's usually with plenty of powder.

In the backcountry, when one can start skiing in earnest is even more weather dependent. I skied knee deep powder on Berthoud Pass on September 23, 2006. However, that was an anomaly. More typically mid-September to mid-October provides only small areas of new snow that are skiable, where wind conditions have blown a 2-3" snowstorm into a skiable base.

For folks like me who try to ski at least one day every month of the year in Colorado, it always becomes difficult to define what is the first day of the new ski season. My rule, though each of my friends have different rules, is that the first day of the ski season is the first day you ski on new snow that is not on top of old snow. So, if St. Mary's Glacier or Andrews Glacier has a fresh inch or two, but not enough to ski above or below the glacier, it doesn't count as the new season; but if there's enough new snow to start fifty yards above the glacier on the new snow, I count it as the first day of the new season.[47]

---

[47] If it's any guide to figuring out when snow typically starts falling in Colorado, using my definition of when the ski season begins, and bearing in mind that I'm nuts about skiing, my first backcountry day of each year from 2010 to 2020 are the following days: October 10, 2010; October 9, 2011; October 14, 2012;

Real chances for powder days – whether inbounds or in the backcountry, begin in earnest in mid-November, but early season conditions often last into mid-December, depending on the year. Although there are powder days before mid-November, there is rarely a sufficient natural base to provide for truly great powder skiing. And even from mid-November to early to mid-December, watch out for stumps and rocks as the snow begins to build the base.

Many Colorado ski resorts open in the second half of November. And practically every resort is open by mid-December. Now that we're in mid-December, let's switch to discussing the winter.

THE WINTER

Winter is the best overall season to chase powder. Duh. Which month in the winter is best to chase powder on average? For many Colorado residents, this question is merely academic as they're around to catch the powder when it comes. But, for the visitors to Colorado, this question is important in trying to determine when to schedule a visit. As will be discussed in Chapter 24 and Appendix B, looking at long-term averages, most places in Colorado tend to see similar total snowfall amounts during each of the four winter months (December, January, February, and March). The main exception is to the east of the continental divide, where there is often a January and February lull, that is made up for in March and April. However, in picking the perfect month, three other factors come into play – total base depth, sun height, and crowds. Let's discuss each in turn.

While December snowfall statistics are roughly the same as the other winter months, there isn't as much of a base of snow below the new snow in December. That means many years not all of the ski areas' terrain, especially in the trees, is open until middle or late December. As Christmas fortunately falls at the end of December, there's pretty good coverage by Christmas almost all, if not quite all, years.

As the winter progresses, the total snow depth increases, making skiing

---

September 24, 2013; October 11, 2014; November 8, 2015; October 9, 2016; October 3, 2017; October 15, 2018; October 12, 2019; October 26, 2020.

better. The total snow base is the deepest in February and March in lower elevations, in March and April at middle elevations, and in April at the highest elevations.

Next, it's worth considering sun height. When winter begins in December, the sun is at its lowest maximum height in the sky, and it has very little ability to turn nice powder into crud. Depending upon elevation, latitude, orientation, and slope angle, the gradual increase in the sun's angle can start to make powder mushy at some point between late-January and early April. The impact of the sun on powder begins at the lower elevations and southern exposures. Where I personally tend to ski (which tends to be high elevation), I usually don't notice the sun baking slopes too often until the month of April begins. Regardless of exact timing, the sun is more likely to have an impact in March than during the colder winter months. However, when considering the pros and cons of March skiing, let's not forget that while occasionally the sun negatively affects the powder in March, at least March provides warmer skiing weather.

The other big question to consider is crowds. If you're hunting powder, you obviously want to compete with fewer people for fresh turns. The busiest times tend to be Christmas to New Years, MLK weekend, Presidents' weekend, and spring break during March. Weekends tend to be busier than weekdays, and this is especially true the closer you get to the major population center of the Denver metropolitan area.

To sum up, during the winter it's hard to pick a wrong time to hunt powder. Overall, January, February, and early-March are probably your best bets in Colorado from a climate perspective. That said, don't forget that this is region dependent, and as will be discussed in more depth in Chapter 24 and Appendix B.

THE SPRING

Come April, the sun gets higher in the sky and the days are warmer, causing more melting. Snow melting is, thankfully, not a quick process. Why? As you may recall from high school science class, the amount of energy needed to melt a certain quantity of ice — that is, to bring 32 degree Fahrenheit ice to 32 degree Fahrenheit water — is the same amount of energy you need to bring that same amount of water all the way up to about 175 degrees Fahrenheit. In other words, if you put old compact snow into a pan and put it on the stove, it'll take roughly the same length of time to melt all the snow as it will take to get the melted snow from freezing cold to almost the boiling point. And, snow being white (for all intents and purposes) means it reflects much of the heating sunlight back towards the sky.

So, snow melt is not a quick process as it requires lots of energy from the warm sun and air. And this leads to great and long-lasting spring skiing.

Fresh snow is still frequent in April. Many of the largest snowstorms, especially in the East of the Continental Divide region, occur in April. Regardless of your location, don't be surprised by April snowstorms, but get after the snow quickly – the warm temperatures and high sun angles turn the powder to mush much quicker than in the middle of winter. Good corn skiing (see Chapter 33) starts in April, and there are many wonderful April corn snow days.

Beware, however, of the day or two after a warm snowstorm (or after it snows and then warms up), when the temperature then swings cold. These cold days after warm snowier days present some of the very few unfun ski days when you leave any well-groomed run. The ungroomed terrain can just be frozen over mush – never fun to ski.

Most of Colorado's ski resorts stay open into the first weekend of April, but most of them also shut down at some point in the month of April. By May 1, most ski areas are closed, but several like A-Basin, Breckenridge, Loveland, and Winter Park, continue to turn their lifts most years into May.

Ironically, at some high-altitude locations like Berthoud Pass, the long-term average maximum snow depth for the whole year is historically on May 1 or May 2 when measured by snow water equivalent. Snowstorms certainly occur in May, but they are rarer than in April. Of the places at which reliable data exists, Berthoud Pass has the highest state-wide average of May snowstorms, averaging 37" in the month of May. More than three feet of snow in the month of May isn't too bad.

By June, only A-Basin remains open of the ski resorts in Colorado, though a plethora of backcountry skiing remains. A-Basin often closes the first weekend of June, but in good snow years, A-Basin often tries to spin its lifts to July 4. In the last three decades, A-Basin was open to July 4 in 1993, 1995, 1996, 1997, 2011, and 2019. A-Basin's record latest closing date was August 10, 1995. So, let's talk about summer next.

THE SUMMER

Bagging Fourteeners seems to be Colorado's most popular outdoor pastime for keeping personal statistics. Most Coloradoans (at least those who love the outdoors) can tell you how many fourteen thousand feet tall mountains they've summited.

In the backcountry skiing community, however, many people obsess more over how many months straight they've had at least one ski day. My current streak of skiing at least one day every month of the year is over a decade long now. The first weekend of July still has many great back-country ski options most years, as discussed in more depth in Chapter 33. By early August, however, only a few reliable spots remain. By September, while finding snow in the Indian Peaks or Rocky Mountain National Park isn't too hard, finding quality snow on which to ski is quite unusual. The September ski day is usually just to keep the streak going, but fear not, by mid-October, A-Basin, Keystone, and Loveland are usually open and the snow is starting to fall all around the state.

Chapter 24

When to Hunt Powder (Part Two) – A Month-by-Month Guide by Region

N ow that we have a statewide season overview, let's dive back into the Colorado snow climate regions to explore the snowiest months by region.

While every ski season is different, long term averages certainly show better and worse months. And, the best months to ski largely depend upon the geographical region (see Chapter 22) that you want to ski. So, let's divide the state into the four regions already discussed, and take a look at the long-term data from the Western Regional Climate Center.

For **Classic Colorado**, snowfall amounts over the long-term tend to be roughly the same from December through March, which are the four snowiest months. This is when those prevailing west winds do their magic trick with orographic lifting and dump foot after foot of snow in the Classic Colorado region. November and April each have less snow, with very little snow in October and May, and virtually no snow the rest of the year. Appendix B provides data for four Classic Colorado locations, Aspen, Powderhorn, Telluride, and Vail.

The **Wolf Creek Pass Area** isn't much different, with the best four months being December, January, February, and March. Appendix B provides the data for this area. While over long-term averages there's a little less snow in February than December, January, or March on Wolf Creek Pass, it still gets a whopping 66.4 inches on average in February, so February is still a fine time to plan a trip.

So far, nothing too surprising, right? Well, let's go to **East of the Continental Divide**. Squaw Mountain, close to Echo Mountain south of Idaho Springs, has the following monthly snowfall pattern by average percentage of yearly total:

September Snowfall:	5%
October Snowfall:	8%
November Snowfall:	10%
December Snowfall:	8%
January Snowfall:	5%
February Snowfall:	9%
March Snowfall:	17%
April Snowfall:	19%
May Snowfall:	14%
June Snowfall:	4%

If you haven't spent a lot of time skiing East of the Divide, this may sound crazy. There's more recorded snowfall in October than January. The month of May logs more snow than November, December, January, or February. In fact, September and January snowfall are about identical. April has more snow than March. Huh?

These numbers can't be right, can they? Well, in Appendix B, I provide the same data for Coal Creek Canyon, not too far from Eldora. Although slightly different, Coal Creek Canyon follows a fairly similar pattern, with an insane one-quarter of the yearly snowfall in the month of April. The months to ski based upon Coal Creek Canyon's long-term numbers are December, March, and April. Likewise, the Mount Evans Research Station averages 60.7 inches of snow in April, and only 24.2 in January. Even in Boulder, where the low elevation makes fall and spring snows less likely, the snowiest month is March and the second snowiest month is November. Indeed, the United States record for the most snow in 24 hours, a record which is still standing nearly one-hundred years after first measured, is 76 inches of snow at Silver Lake, five miles due north of Eldora, during a 24-hour period spanning April 14 and 15, 1921. While numbers vary, the pattern stays the same through the East of the Continental Divide region – snowy autumns, relatively dry winters, and whopping snowfalls come springtime.

Why is this? Well, the answer is a little complicated, so let's start with discussing a figure-skater. (Yes, I can hear you yelling – "I'm a skier. I know about skiing, and I know about beer. So, explaining the science of recycled powder by discussing beer makes sense to me. But I don't know anything about figure skating!" Well, I'm sorry. You're just going to have to put up with the figure skater analogy because I haven't been able to come up with a good beer analogy as of yet.)

Anyone who has seen a figure skater do a spin knows that if the figure skater brings her arms and legs in close to her center she'll spin faster. But, if she scrunches down putting her arms and legs out, her spin will slow down. We don't need to get into the science of the conservation of angular momentum to get the concept. When a skater, or a rotating weather system, is spread out wider, she / it rotates more slowly. As a low pressure moves over the Rocky Mountains, it must slow down because literally there is less room between the ground and the top of our layer of the atmosphere, the top of the troposphere, for the system to rotate. As soon as the low pressure passes the Rocky Mountains, the entire air column in which it can operate is now significantly taller as the ground is so much lower. It's the equivalent of the figure skater scrunched up passing over the Rocky Mountains but then getting taller again as she gets onto the plains, allowing her to spin faster once past the mountains.

Spin means lift. And lift means snow. You don't believe me? Here's a beer analogy, pour the beer you're drinking right now out of its can or bottle and into a mug. Then, spin the mug in your hands. The faster you spin the mug, the more the beer at the center of the mug seems to funnel downwards. But please do this sober, so as not to waste beer by spilling it all over yourself. You've literally created a low pressure system in your beer mug – where the faster the spin, the lower the pressure is in the center of the mug. As we learned in Chapter 4, low pressure means air will lift. And rising air means the air will cool and it will snow.

Literally, the lee side (i.e., the downwind side) of the Rocky Mountains create low pressure systems because the air column can become tall enough to spin faster. These are called Colorado lows (if they come from Colorado) or Alberta clippers (if they come from the lee side of the Canadian Rockies, which is in the Canadian Province of Alberta). And folks in the Midwest who do not ski complain about the snowstorms generated by the Colorado lows and the Alberta clippers.

Hang in there folks, now that you get the basic concept of why low pressure systems form (or more technically re-form) along Colorado's Front Range, I'm almost halfway through explaining why it snows a lot in the spring and fall in the East of the Continental Divide region. Do you remember how we discussed in Chapter 8 that bigger temperature contrasts make a faster jet stream? In the summer, temperatures aren't that different between Detroit and Dallas. They're both bloody hot. So, the upper-level winds don't move as fast and the jet stream is far to the north. During the winter, however, Detroit is cold but Dallas is still hot, so the jet stream moves much faster, and runs from west to east in a wave pattern somewhere between Detroit and Dallas. Well, this means that during the winter, the fast-moving jet stream and upper air currents quickly drive the newly formed Colorado lows into the Midwest. These storms are blown away too quickly to produce much snow in Colorado's Front Range. However, in the fall and in the spring, when the temperature contrast between Detroit and Dallas (or whichever northerly and southerly city you'd like to pick) isn't as much, the jet stream isn't moving as fast and is often further north. What does that mean? The Colorado lows, instead of being quickly dispatched by the jet stream to clobber the Midwest with snow, instead tend to meander in Colorado for a while. This produces snow. And this is why the relatively warmer month of March is the snowiest month in Boulder, and why the also relatively warmer month of November is the second snowiest month in Boulder.

Okay, we're almost there to understanding why the fall and spring produce the biggest snow in places like Echo Mountain, Eldora Mountain, and the popular backcountry skiing spots in Rocky Mountain National Park, which are all in the East of the Continental Divide region. Let's throw the last key concept into the mix. What is the biggest snow producer? Orographic lifting! What creates orographic lifting that pummels the areas east of the continental divide, like Echo Mountain, Eldora, and Rocky Mountain National Park? We discussed this in depth in Chapters 3 and 4. It's the wind blowing from east to west. The Colorado lows that formed in the Colorado Front Range, are rotating counterclockwise. Everything to the north of the center of the low pressure system is seeing wind blowing from east to west. So, combining the snow the low pressure system is already producing by its own lift, with the orographic lift from the winds blowing from east to west, Echo, Eldora, and Rocky Mountain National Park can get clobbered with snow. And, often moisture from the Gulf can get sucked into this rotating wind, which will help increase the total of the storm's moisture. For those readers who love to ski to the East of the Continental Divide region, I bet you never knew that you owe it all to the conservation of angular momentum.

So now you can forget figure skating, but you can keep swirling your beer, and keep reading.

What about the **Continental Divide** region? As we've learned, fall and spring storms tend to batter the East Side of the Continental Divide region (which means spillover just to the west of the continental divide in those storms). And, winter storms tend to batter the Classic Colorado region, which are to the west of the continental divide (which means spillover just to the east of the continental divide). So, regardless of the storm track, the continental divide picks up something, which means that the Continental Divide region tends to see the high autumn and especially spring snows coming from the East of the Continental Divide region, while also seeing the winter storms coming from the Classic Colorado region. In other words, Berthoud Pass and Loveland Pass receive both the Vail winter storms and the Eldora spring storms. As the location we're looking at moves further from the continental divide towards the Classic Colorado region, its snow patterns start to resemble more of Classic Colorado than the top of the Continental Divide. Appendix B compares Berthoud Pass, Winter Park, and Breckenridge from this region.

In sum, it snows the most at Vail in the winter, at Eldora in the fall and spring, and Berthoud Pass every season but summer.

Chapter 25

When to Decide Where to Ski Based Upon Forecasts

A s a college student and a ski patroller in the 1990s, deciding when and where to ski was an easy task – every weekend day I would ski and patrol at my home hill (first Eldora and then the since-closed Berthoud Pass Ski Area) unless a ski patrol clinic brought me to another resort. Weather forecasts made virtually no difference in choosing when and where to ski. At that time, teaching avalanche safety classes, I would joke that I would happily teach any topic in our avalanche classes except weather.

It's amazing how times change as you grow older. With a fun but stressful full-time job and two children, planning when and where to ski ahead of time is far more important. Here's a typical scenario. I can block off from work either Tuesday or Thursday morning next week to ski as long as I block it off now. Which day should I choose? Or, which of the two weekend days should I plan to take the kids skiing, ideally with sunny and pleasant conditions, while which weekend days should I go skiing with my backcountry buddies, ideally with deep powder and cold conditions? With the current storm cycle, should I try to sneak down to Taos or up to Steamboat for the weekend?

All of a sudden, predicting the weather has become far more important. So, with that in mind, let's discuss how far away from your ski day you can figure out the likely snow conditions. Let's start in forecast fairyland.

Preseason – From the Farmer's Almanac to individual forecasters, many people attempt to predict in August or September how snowy Colorado's winter will be. My advice? Ignore these forecasts. Ignore them completely. Year after year if you look back at the preseason forecasts for the winter compared to what actually occurred that winter, there is no correlation. You'd be better off simply sticking with the climate data – that is, the average winter – in predicting any upcoming winter.

As these forecasts for months ahead have no correlation with the actual winter, you can similarly ignore all talk of El Niño and La Niña (or to be more technically accurate, the El Niño-Southern Oscillation or ENSO). While El Niño and La Niña are real, and they have major repercussions (some of which correlate to weather in maritime areas), there simply is not a real correlation between El Niño, La Niña, and Colorado snow. (I'm sure I'll get hate mail for having said this, but it's true!) And, you can certainly ignore all the old-wives' tales about what a winter will be like. Here are some of my favorite fictional old-wives' tales. New Zealand winters predict the upcoming Colorado winters. False. An earlier start to fall colors means a snowier winter. False. An earlier start to Elk bugling means a snowier winter. False. And, an early season big snowfall means a bigger snow winter. Also false. These tales may be fun to tell, but they are not science.

18 days out – 18 days before your potential ski day, the only useful information you have will be likely consolidated snow depth, not conditions on your planned ski day. You can legitimately ask yourself – are the Southern Mountains having a good snow year, so there will be a great base of snow to ski on regardless of whether there is fresh powder? Current snow depth data and/or a general understanding of how the winter has been so far will quickly apprise you of this information. Beyond the ski area's snow report on its website, which is very helpful, the National Water and Climate Center also maintains a system of Snotel sites throughout the state, which provide data on current snow depths as measured by the machine systems throughout the mountains of Colorado.[48] Although many sites provide the snow

---

[48]   This information is free and publicly available at: https://www. nrcs.usda.gov/wps/portal/nrcs/detailfull/co/snow/waterproducts/ basin/?cid=NRCSEPRD1308237.

depth not in inches of snow but in inches of snow water equivalent – the sites all compare current conditions to historical averages so you can know right away if that site is at 80% or 120% of its historical average for that date.

If you want, however, to gain information 18 days out on whether it will be snowy or clear on your planned ski day or if there will be 1 inch of fresh powder or 12 inches of fresh powder, I'm sorry. 18 days out is way off in forecast fairyland, and you might as well check your horoscope or consult with Punxsutawney Phil. We're many decades away from being able to predict weather that far out with any accuracy.

12 days out – 12 days before your potential ski day, several of the medium-term global computer models are offering weather forecasts. Sorry, however, you are still far off in forecast fairyland. The forecasts out at this range are no better than simply using the historical averages for the date (that is, climate data). The Butterfly Effect is just too powerful and overwhelms the models. However, as scientific knowledge and computing power increases, it may be within our lifetimes that a 12-day forecast can come into the realm of a meaningful forecast. At current trends in improved forecasting, I'll likely be an old man when the models will be making somewhat reliable forecasts out to 12 days. But hey, here's to hoping it will happen sooner.

6 days out – 6 days before your potential ski day, we have left forecast fairyland, if just barely, and we're starting to enter the realm where the science of meteorology can start to guide your decisions. Six days away may be too far out to know whether you'll get 2 inches or 10 inches, but it will let you know if it is more likely than not that it will be stormy, and which way the storm track may be headed. Open Snow and the National Weather Service are providing forecast discussions that include what will most likely be happening six days out. This may be the first time you can start to make an educated guess if you should spend the weekend in Taos or Steamboat. But be prepared, there's a good chance the forecast will turn out completely wrong this far out.

Unless you are looking at many models yourself, pay attention as you read forecast discussions to how much confidence the forecaster has in his or her forecast. As you'll recall from Chapter 11, one of the keys to weather prediction is to see if the various models and model runs are agreeing or disagreeing with each other. If all major models are calling for a stormy period in Colorado, there's a good chance it will be stormy. But if the models are all over the map (no pun intended), or if each new model run produces vastly different results from the immediately prior run, it's hard to have much confidence in the forecast. All forecasters worth their salt will provide in their forecast discussion their confidence in their prediction when predicting this far in the future.

3 days out – By 3 days before your potential ski day, the forecast should start becoming more reliable. You're within range of almost every computer model for weather forecasting. Not only are the medium-term global models providing forecasts, most of the short-term regional models are providing forecasts too. There are a lot more data points which the forecasters can analyze. The storms often are forming or have formed already over the ocean. So, conditions from where the storm is coming are becoming more clear. While you may get a surprise powder day or you may get skunked, you can start to form meaningful decisions on whether going one day earlier or one day later will make a difference.

1 1/2 days out – By the time you are one and half days out from your ski day, not only is Open Snow and the National Weather Service providing forecast discussions, even the CAIC is providing a detailed forecast discussion. The models are getting more reliable. And any storm itself is actually on its way to Colorado by this point. With multiple sources and multiple models, you can make relatively reliable decisions on where and when to go.

The morning of – It's game time! All of a sudden weather forecasts mean less (except for figuring out how snowy the drive home will be), because you will know where it did and did not snow overnight. Most ski areas post their snow reports between 5 and 6 am. Perhaps even better, the snow depth webcams that most Colorado ski areas have online give you this information immediately. And many of these snow depth webcams have a 24-hour play feature, so you can see when it was snowing and how hard over the last

24 hours. Be sure you know when the ski area clears its snow depth web-cam, as you'd hate to check it at 6:30 am and see only a half an inch, when in reality it snowed a foot overnight but was cleared at 6 am.

Webcams and to some extent snow reports are the gold standard for knowing how much it snowed. If you're a backcountry skier, however, you can always access the Snotel data, discussed above, to learn new snow amounts. While neither source is perfect, see Chapter 18, you'll have a pretty good idea of where the best places are to go. You can now intelligently decide which ski area or backcountry spot you should head to for the best powder that day. Enjoy!

Chapter 26

Pointers for a Powder Day at a Ski Resort

Everyone has their own techniques and plans for maximizing their powder experience at a ski resort. Here are eighteen of my pointers, for what they are worth, on how to get the best powder at Colorado's ski resorts on any given powder day.

1. **First Chair.** This almost goes without saying, but your odds of getting a good powder day are drastically increased by showing up early. There is nothing wrong with standing in line well before the lift first opens. If you're among the first hundred people riding the lift, your first run will be amazing. And, if it's a mountain that you can ski halfway down and catch a higher lift, your second run is guaranteed to be amazing too. You won't even have to work at getting great powder. So, show up a little early.
2. **Sides, Not Center.** The center of ski runs get skied off long before the sides of the run do. If your ski skills are good enough so you know you can avoid the trees (and you know and are careful about tree wells), the sides of the runs will offer you more powder than the center of runs.
3. **Trees, Not Runs.** Runs get skied off long before the trees between them get skied. Assuming you're a proficient tree skier and respect tree wells, the trees will always offer more powder than the runs.

4. **Steeper Feels Deeper.** Six inches of powder on a blue run does not ski as deep as six inches of powder on a double black run. Often, the steeper the slope, the nicer and deeper the powder feels. This is largely based upon your body's position in the snow as you ski down steeper runs. The drift of snow into steeper terrain and the wind deposition of snow in steeper terrain often help as well, and there's at least some scientific evidence that orographic snowfall is greater on steeper terrain. Setting aside the avalanche issues of steeper terrain (see Chapter 27), there is another big caveat on the rule of skiing the steeper terrain on a powder day, which I'll discuss next.

5. **But Mellow Beats Steep.** Let's face it, the better a skier is, the more he or she likes powder. So, this means that the black and double-black runs and their nearby trees get skied-out much quicker than the intermediate runs and their nearby trees. While beginner runs and their nearby trees are usually too mellow to enjoy powder, the still somewhat mellow blue terrain is a better source for reliable powder than the blacks and double blacks. Mary Jane may be completely skied out when the intermediate trees of Winter Park still have untouched powder.

6. **Pick Your Resorts Carefully.** Just as better skiers tend to stick to the blacks and thus ski the powder out on them before the blues, better skiers tend to prefer the tougher resorts on powder days. This means your odds of getting more powder are at the easier ski resorts. You'll be competing with fewer gung-ho powder skiers if you ski Keystone as opposed to Breckenridge; Buttermilk as opposed to Aspen Highlands; and Granby Ranch as opposed to Winter Park.

7. **Don't Fear the Hike.** Skiers can be lazy, so only a five-minute hike will eliminate 90% or more of the skiers. Let's face it, you have to carry your skis from the car to the lift already, so what's wrong with hiking for five to ten minutes to get better powder? Assuming the resort has specifically designated hike-to terrain, those areas will provide you with powder that will last much longer.

8. **Stick with the Fixed Gripped Lifts.** There's an old joke that the best lift for skiing at every ski area is a fixed grip double – Challenger

at Winter Park, Pallavicini at A-Basin, Chair 14 at Mammoth, etc. While this is a questionable proposition, detachable (i.e., high speed) lifts can transport more people than fixed grip (i.e., regular speed) lifts, so you'll be competing against fewer skiers if you're skiing in an area serviced only by fixed grip lifts.

9. **Know the Patrol.** Back when I worked at the old Berthoud Pass Ski Area, we'd start letting the public getting off the lift know about five minutes before we opened any new gates to access new terrain. While this practice is no longer in vogue in the open Colorado ski resorts, there's never any harm of asking any and every ski patroller you see what the plan for the day will be – when and in what order they plan to open gates. There's nothing better than having skied great powder from 8:30 am to 10:00 am, relaxing on a few groomers from 10:00 am to 11:00 am, and having your legs ready at 11:00 am when ski patrol opens a gate accessing more untouched powder. I've even known a few people (and please don't do this) who have listened in on patrol radios to figure out terrain openings before anyone else.

10. **Weekdays, not Weekends.** There are a lot of skiers who live in Colorado. (Sorry about that, to those of you who are visiting our fair state.) What does that mean? If you're coming from out-of-state, or have a flexible work schedule, weekdays offer better powder days than weekend days because you're competing with fewer people. This is especially true the closer the ski resort is to the population center of Denver. Simply, Tuesdays are terrific and Wednesdays are wonderful.

11. **Have Patience.** Depending upon the ski area and the amount of snowfall, it can take considerable time to open terrain (and the lifts accessing the terrain) owing to avalanche mitigation efforts by ski patrol. At ski areas with more significant avalanche risk, it is not atypical for the best powder day to be not the morning after the storm, but the following morning when avalanche mitigation work has finally been completed and most if not all lifts can be opened.

12. **South and Southeast before North and West.** If you think there will be enough snow to last all day, or for several days, it's worth considering which aspects will get sunbaked first. This is of particular importance from mid-March onwards. South and southeast facing runs simply turn mushy from the sun before north and west facing slopes. So, the powder in the south facing back bowls of Vail will get sunbaked before the north facing Blue Sky Basin and Front Side of Vail. So, in the spring, enjoy the back bowls first, while they're still good.

13. **Leeward is Better than Windward.** Especially in the windier parts of Colorado, the slopes that are on the leeward side of the storm (i.e., the downwind side) as opposed to the windward side of the storm (i.e., the upwind side) tend to have better powder as the wind blows the deeper snow onto the leeward side. With the normal winds from the west, the windward is the west facing slopes and the leeward is the east facing slopes. With an upslope storm, which means the winds come from the east, the windward is east facing and the leeward is west facing.

14. **Left Before Right for North Facing Runs.** As explained in detail in Chapter 19, with a storm from the west, the skier's left sides on the north faces and the skier's right sides on the south faces are usually better. The opposite is true if the storm came from the east. What if the storm comes from the north or south? If you were paying attention in Chapter 19, you'll know the answer. This isn't rocket science.

15. **The Treeline Question.** To ski above treeline or not to ski above treeline, that is the question. Many of Colorado's resorts have terrain above treeline. Once there are no longer trails, so to speak, but rather just large expanses of snow to ski, this permits wider areas for people to find powder. On the other hand, these wide expanses permit the wind to blow off all the freshly fallen powder. But on the other hand (I guess I must have three hands), wind can likewise turn a 2" day into a 20" day if you know the right spot that's getting wind loaded above treeline. Simply, the question of whether to ski above

or below the treeline is so snow and wind-dependent, it can't be answered in the abstract. Pay attention to each storm to determine where is best.

16. **Understanding Local Topography.** It seems that for every six inches at the front side of Keystone Mountain, there's a foot of snow on the Outback of Keystone. This is one of countless examples of how slight topographical and elevation differences can make tremendous differences in the amount of powder. Many of Colorado's ski areas are so vast that there are major snowfall differences within the ski area itself. Learning the snow patterns of your home ski area (or if you're at a relatively new ski area for you, asking ski patrol for advice on where snow tends to accumulate), will help you to find the better powder. And even within a single ski run, minor topographical differences can mean drastically better powder in some spots than others – so study up on Chapter 19.

17. **Making Your Own Luck.** Let's be honest, sometimes luck plays a major factor in finding the perfect powder spot on any particular day. But as Professor Richard Wiseman's studies on luck have shown, people do really create their own luck by looking for opportunities, following their intuition, and remaining positive. So, pray to Poli'ahu (the Hawaiian Goddess of Snow), Ullr (the Norse God of Snow), or whoever your deity of choice is for good powder. But look for those powder opportunities. And stay positive – you're out powder hunting, after all!

18. **Think Different.** Economist John Maynard Keynes had an analogy for picking stocks with a fictional beauty contest, where people are asked to pick the most beautiful six faces from hundreds of photographs. But the catch is that the entrants must pick the most popular faces, not the ones they themselves think are the most beautiful. So, a rational entrant instead of picking the six faces he or she thinks are the most beautiful, will choose the six faces he or she thinks everyone else will choose. At this point, you're probably asking yourself, why am I reading about economics in a book about skiing powder? Hang in there, I'll get to the point shortly. Keynes

used this analogy to explain the stock market – an investor is trying to buy the stocks he or she thinks everyone else will like, not the ones he or she personally likes. The opposite of this analogy is perfect for powder hunting.

When you're competing with thousands of other people at the ski area for fresh powder, think about where the average powder hunter would go to ski powder (i.e., the most popular prettiest face), and don't go there. Rather, you should choose the face you think is the prettiest who you also think no one else will think is the prettiest. Does the average person think the Back Bowls at Vail will have the best powder on a powder day? Then, ski the Wildwood or Avanti lifts at Vail. Or drive to Ski Cooper. Think different than the masses. But no matter what you do, don't go into closed terrain. And, if you're in any doubt whether or not an area is closed, to be safe, you should assume it is closed.

Summing It Up. From reading this, it quickly becomes clear that on a good powder day, there's an order to skiing the terrain. On the first run (hopefully right after the lifts started spinning), ski the center of the run. If by your second or third run, the centers of the runs are skied out, move to the sides of the run. If there's still plenty of fresh powder on both sides, ski the side closest to where the winds are blowing from. When the sides of runs are skied out, leave the runs and head for the black diamond trees. When those are skied out, head to the blue square trees. Be ready to catch new terrain as it opens, and don't hesitate to hike when the hike-to terrain opens. Happy powder hunting!

PART 7

THE DANGERS

Okay, I know reading about dangers of powder hunting is not fun. But it is important. The dangers of the mountains are almost countless – some very common like driving on icy roads on the way to your favorite ski resort; while others are very unlikely but still possible, like a moose attack while skiing. This book addresses only a few of the myriad of dangers and focuses for a large part on those inherent risks involving snow, e.g., avalanches, snow immersion suffocations, etc.

This book is, after all, about hunting powder, so I thought it should address the most infamous danger of snow first: avalanches. The following chapter will be on the less well known but still quite dangerous tree well / snow immersion suffocation risks; followed by a discussion of cornices and also glacial dangers; followed by a discussion of the fall/collision risk; and finishing with a chapter on the environmental and exposure risks.

Obviously, this part by no means covers all the dangers of skiing powder (or skiing corn, groomers, or sand). And, it can only skim the surface of the dangers that are discussed. Please read, study, and learn more about all of the dangers.

Most of the folks I ski with, like me, have lost at least one friend or family member to the mountains. It's heartbreaking, and I tear up just thinking about those we've lost. We all want to come home alive and well after every ski trip, so please be careful, be knowledgeable, be cognizant of the risks, and use good judgment out there.

Chapter 27

Avalanches

M y first close encounter with an avalanche happened near Berthoud Pass in the mid-90s while backcountry skiing. I was a 20-year-old college student at CU Boulder, and as a ski patroller and avid outdoorsman, I should have known what I was doing. A combination of ignorance and testosterone almost turned an amazing early season powder day into a disaster. As my group of friends and I took our first two runs in the newly fallen knee-deep backcountry snow, we saw one of the most tell-tale signs of high avalanche danger – shooting cracks. But we ignored it. With each run we skied steeper pitches.

With all of us ignoring one of mother nature's biggest warning signs, on the third run I ventured ahead of my colleagues. Right before the 38-degree pitch run known as Hanging Meadow, I made a quick hockey stop to wait for my friends. Stopping right above the steep pitch, the entire slope just below and beyond my skis broke, and I watched in horror as the snow went hurdling out of sight in the rush of an avalanche. A few seconds later, I could see a cloud of snow rise, as the avalanche hit the trees below the run. I was only a few feet away from having been swept into the avalanche and had I been, I could have been easily buried or thrown into the trees at the bottom of the avalanche path. I was lucky. A mere five months later, another 20-year-old CU student wasn't so lucky.

On a random Sunday five months later, I was working as a ski patroller at the old Berthoud Pass Ski Area. I had just completed my Level II Avalanche training a few weeks before, and after my early season avalanche scare and much subsequent training, I was much more in the avalanche mindset. About mid-day that Sunday, the call came on the patrol radio that sent a shiver down my spine. The radio transmission, as best as I recall, sounded something like this: "Avalanche. There's been a report of an out-of-bounds avalanche. Still confirming, but it sounds like one snowboarder is buried. All patrollers, except for whoever is sitting east side coverage, please go to the first aid room immediately." Every patroller with Level II Avalanche training, save one to dispatch, formed the immediate search team to head to the avalanche debris field. I was the most junior member of that seven-person team.

Roughly an hour and a half after that initial radio call, I was on a gigantic avalanche debris field, less than a mile away from where I set off the avalanche early season, shoveling vigorously to clear the buried snowboarder's face. Although we had six strong ski patrollers all shoveling, and within a few minutes of digging we could access the snowboarder's neck and feel that he had no carotid pulse, it took us a painfully long time (what felt like 15 minutes) to dig him out sufficiently so we could unstrap his snowboard and flip him over to begin CPR. I did chest compressions for nearly an hour while we waited for a toboggan to arrive. Once the toboggan arrived, one of the female patrollers on the scene, who was much lighter than me, took over chest compressions while I helped haul the toboggan with the deceased snowboarder and two patrollers doing CPR to a waiting ambulance on the road. I learned later from the news reports that the snowboarder had been a twenty-year-old CU Boulder student, just like me.

Just as I had made every mistake in the book earlier that season, he (on a snowboard) and his companion (on skis) made every mistake later that season. They chose to ski a major avalanche path when conditions weren't relatively safe. They skied the run at the same time – so neither could spot the other as the avalanche swept them both down the mountain. They didn't have avalanche beacons, shovels, or probes, so when the skier ended up on the surface and the snowboarder ended up buried, the skier couldn't quickly locate the snowboarder. And, the skier (understandably but wrongly) panicked and went out to get help as opposed to searching for his friend. Most people dug out shortly after an avalanche stops survive. The survival chance is less than ten percent, however, if the rescue is over an hour. And in the backcountry setting, a formal rescue is almost always longer than an hour.

Like me earlier in the year, he was skiing a large avalanche path on a day with significant avalanche danger, with neither an appreciation of the risk nor following any of the proper avalanche terrain travel protocols. I skied away physically unscathed. He didn't survive.

Both of us were young, aggressive, strong skiers/snowboarders, and made poor decisions. Avalanches, however, have no personality or consciousness. They do not care whom they strike. The next person I dug out from under avalanche debris was a thirty-year-old woman. Based upon her location and the subsequent news reports, I assume that she thought she was just out for a mellow day of snowshoeing near Jones Pass. She did not survive either.

Colorado, sadly, leads the nation in avalanche fatalities. We have a combination of a high population who enjoys the wonders of our outdoor environment coupled with one of the most dangerous snowpacks in the world. This means that avalanche safety should be foremost on Colorado skiers' minds.

This short chapter can in no way prepare someone to travel in backcountry terrain, but it hopefully provides an overview (or a brief refresher) on avalanche safety. If you haven't taken official avalanche classes yet, taking them is an absolute necessity before venturing into the backcountry. And, it's good for any powder skier to know the basics of avalanche safety. Four factors lead to avalanches – terrain, snowpack, weather (which is already the subject of a large portion of this book), and the addition of people into that mix. I'll discuss terrain, snowpack, and the human element, in turn, in this chapter.

Terrain – No matter how bad the weather or snowpack might be, if a slope is flat, it won't avalanche. Rather, the angle of the terrain has to be steep enough to avalanche. The simplest experiment can show this – take one book and put it on top of another book, and put them on a desk. The top book doesn't slide off the bottom book. Then, start putting objects (pencils, a stapler, or whatever) between one side of the bottom book and desk, to increase the angle of the books. At some angle, the top book will slide off the bottom book. This is the same with avalanches. Snow, for all intents and purposes, will not slide at 25 degrees. But, at 35 degrees, it will almost certainly slide given the wrong snowpack conditions.

Although avalanches on rare occasion occur on less steep slopes, as a general rule of thumb, avalanches do not start on slopes less than 30 degrees.[49] Remember, 30 degrees! There is one gigantic caveat to this over 30-degree rule. It applies to where the avalanche starts. An avalanche starting on a steep slope can run onto flatter ground – indeed occasionally the biggest avalanches can run down one side of the mountain, into the valley floor, and slightly up the mountain on the other side of the valley. So, the key is always not only to look at the angle of the slope you are on, but also the angle of the slope above you, to figure out if you're in an avalanche path.

The best way to figure out how steep 30 degrees is, is to go out and buy an inclinometer, or simply download an inclinometer app on your smartphone, and start measuring every slope you ski. Pretty soon you will get comfortable with the absolutely critical dividing line between below 30 degrees and above 30 degrees terrain.

As a very rough rule of thumb, blue runs at ski areas are between 20-30 degrees, black diamond runs are between 30 and 35 degrees, and double-black diamonds are over 35 degrees. However, as every ski area differs in how they rate their runs, the far better method is to start measuring ski slopes with which you're familiar to get a sense of slope angle.

When my father took his first avalanche class, once he learned the over 30-degree rule, he didn't need to learn anything more about avalanches as he simply learned how to spot a 30 degree slope, and made sure not to go on or under such a slope. And, if you only like to ski mellow terrain, or only like to snowshoe, this is a great approach to avoiding most avalanche risk.

Unfortunately, the best skiing for expert skiers tends to be in the 35-to-40-degree range. This is prime avalanche slope angle. In fact, 38.5 degrees is the angle at which continental snow is most likely to avalanche, which is a

---

[49] Many avalanche books teach people that avalanches most typically occur on slopes between 30 and 45 degrees. However, the upper limit, 45 degrees, is largely superfluous to Colorado skiers. Our wonderfully light continental snow has great difficulty sticking to slopes steeper than about 45 degrees. So, it's rare that people ski slopes much steeper than 45 degrees in Colorado, except for the first few turns coming off a cornice or the remnants of a cornice.

perfect pitch for great powder skiing. As deep powder and steep slopes are a recipe not only for great skiing, but also for avalanches, skiers (especially backcountry skiers) need to carefully study avalanche science if they want to ski fun terrain.

A few more thoughts on terrain. Be wary of terrain traps – that is, an avalanche path above a cliff (where even a small avalanche could send you over a cliff), an avalanche path through tight trees (where an avalanche would be slamming you into trees), or above a steep valley/ravine (where even a small avalanche could create a deep burial area). And don't forget that even a small avalanche can be deadly – people have died from avalanches starting on the top of roofs of houses.

Snowpack – We already went through much of the basics of snow science in Chapter 20 on recycled powder. Remember – where do you bury beer in the snowpack? At the ground because the ground is the warmest spot. Remember how there are two major types of snow created by snow metamorphosis – *facets* and **rounds**? Facets form when there is a large temperature difference between the cold nighttime surface of the snow and the warmer ground. If there's not a large temperature gradient, rounds form. If you don't remember the details, before reading on, you may want to review Chapter 20 again.

Facets (a/k/a recycled powder when the facets are on the surface of the snowpack) are large crystals that don't bond together well – you can't make snowballs out of them as they'd just fall apart. They're commonly called sugar snow, and that's how they feel. Rounds, on the other hand, would make great snowballs if the snowpack was warmer. Rounds are a lot more solid.

What is dangerous is not rounds per se, or facets per se, but when a layer of rounds is sitting on a buried layer of facets. This is the equivalent of putting a heavy book on a house of cards. It's hard for the facet layer to keep the round layer from sliding. When on the surface, facets can make for excellent skiing – especially if the facets are fairly deep – as discussed in Chapter 20. But once they are buried by new snow, facets become dangerous.

In fact, one of the reasons why Colorado's snowpack is so dangerous, is because we have such cold nights. Facets just form better in our snowpack than in most other mountainous places in the world.

While buried facets are dangerous, the most dangerous buried snow layer is a peculiar but unfortunately common type of snow similar to facets, called ***surface hoar***. Surface hoar are giant faceted snow crystals, formed on the snow surface on cold clear and relatively windless nights. The water vapor in the air just above the snow surface deposits onto the snow surface at night forming long crystals. Once buried by subsequent snowstorms, surface hoar layers are responsible for more Colorado avalanche fatalities than any other layer.

Below is a photograph of sparkly surface hoar taken in the morning after it formed overnight.

Another dangerous layer are *ice lenses*, which are often caused by sun crust. These ice crusts are typically warmer than the surrounding buried snow. As they are warmer (i.e., closer to 32 degrees Fahrenheit / 0 Celsius) while the snow on either side of them are colder, they encourage facet growth directly above and below them once buried in the snowpack. And when temperatures warm, typically later in the season, free water in the snowpack can often run down through the snowpack until they hit the ice lens. As the free water cannot penetrate the ice lens, it instead runs along the top of the lens removing all support from the upper snowpack.

In short, beware of rounds or new snow on top of facets. Beware of rounds or new snow on top of surface hoar. And beware of rounds or new snow on top of ice lenses.

Human Element – Hundreds of thousands of avalanches run naturally every year in Colorado, without anyone being hurt or anyone even noticing. Avalanches only matter when a person is present. Typically, when a person is killed in an avalanche, he or she is the one who triggered the avalanche.

So, what triggers avalanches? They can run naturally from the snowpack being overwhelmed by snow, wind, or a cornice collapse. Avalanches can be triggered by explosives – as both ski patrollers and the Colorado Department of Transportation do for mitigation purposes. Or, avalanches can be triggered by people in the mountains, whether on skis, snowboard, snowmobile, snowshoe, or otherwise. The vast majority of people who die in avalanches either triggered the avalanche themselves, or someone in their own group triggered the avalanche.

When travelling in avalanche terrain in the backcountry, you should be mindful of where the avalanche terrain is, as discussed above, and avoid that terrain as much as possible. In an ironic twist, the best skiing is often fresh powder on steep slopes, which are two of the things one should avoid in order to avoid avalanche danger. So, many people want (when it is comparatively safe) to expose themselves to avalanche terrain to ski great steep snow. How does one do this?

First, you should take official avalanche classes and you should spend lots of time carefully studying avalanche science both in the field and in the classroom.

Second, you should travel with other knowledgeable and equipped people, and be willing to turn around and head back to the car if anyone in the group is not comfortable.

Third, you should avoid avalanche terrain (including the run-out zones) whenever possible. When not possible (usually because you want to ski an avalanche path), expose only one person from your group at a time to the avalanche terrain.

Fourth, you should carry appropriate gear – beacon, shovel, and probe are a minimum; and most backcountry skiers today also use airbags. And, not only should you carry this gear, but you should also know how to use it and how to conduct avalanche searches should someone in your group get buried. By the time ski patrol or search and rescue arrives, they are usually doing a body recovery. So, the survival of a buried person usually depends upon the skill of those they are skiing with.

ADDITIONAL THOUGHTS

You should remember that often the most dangerous places to ski are where the snow is the best. While writing Chapter 19 on wind impact on snow, I realized that I was giving the opposite advice to what I give when teaching avalanche classes. It's like writing a book on storm chasing while teaching classes on how to avoid storms. This is a book on how to find powder and deep snow, but in bad terrain, this powder and deep snow can turn deadly.

Unlike weather forecasting – where an incorrect forecast usually just means that you'll either get skunked with less snow than you thought or pleasantly surprised by more snow than you thought – your own forecasting of the avalanche danger on any particular run you are about to ski holds the consequences of your life. This is scary. On average, depending upon the study and location, your odds of dying in an avalanche you trigger are very roughly 10%. So, if you make one avalanche forecasting mistake every year, your life expectancy will be rather short. This concept terrifies me as I ski so many backcountry avalanche paths (usually several hundred of varying sizes per year). This means that if I'm ever wrong in my prediction that the path I'm going to ski won't slide, a single error will mean that I have a 10% chance of never coming home. I haven't made an error resulting in a real slide since the backcountry avalanche story that began this chapter. However, it's a constant fear, especially as I know all too well that I am fallible. I constantly study avalanche science, try to keep learning, and try to play it very safe. You should too.

Also, while this discussion is mostly geared towards the backcountry, it should be noted that avalanches pay no attention to ski area boundary ropes. While ski patrols work extraordinarily hard in minimizing avalanche risk, it is impossible to eliminate completely avalanche risk from ski areas. When skiing steep avalanche terrain in ski areas, or travelling below such steep terrain, be aware there are risks, even if they are statistically much lower than the risks in the backcountry. While there have been less than a handful of in-bound open terrain avalanche fatalities in Colorado in the last twenty-years, they do occasionally occur.[50] And be especially vigilant to stay out of closed terrain, as terrain is often closed due to avalanche danger or to perform avalanche work.

---

[50]   The few numbers are both a testament to the vigilance of ski patrollers and also a result of the fact that facets are less likely to form on heavily compacted slopes as explained in Chapter 20.

Chapter 28

Snow Immersion Suffocation

A valanche fatalities make the news far more than snow immersion suffocations, and the term avalanche is far more known than snow immersion suffocations. Heck, our hockey team is named after avalanches. It's hard to imagine a hockey team named the Snow Immersion Suffocations.

Snow immersion suffocations (also known as tree well fatalities), however, are a real and deadly danger of powder skiing. From 2001 to 2020, there were fourteen snow immersion suffocation fatalities in Colorado. Colorado is second only to California in the number of fatalities.

Tree wells often form in Colorado. A tree well is the comparatively hollow space surrounding the trunk of a tree. The tree branches help support the snow and create an environment of air, ice, and vegetation. Contributing to the loose or missing snow around the trunk of a tree is the fact that trees are comparatively as warm compared to the nearby snow, which causes a large temperature gradient and faceting of the snow crystals. (See Chapter 20). As such, the snow around the tree is loose and uncompacted. Fir trees can be particularly dangerous. Ones even as small as the typical Christmas tree can be deadly.

Tree wells create a danger when someone falls into one. And, this danger is often life-threatening when a person falls headfirst, which can often entrap the skier. Making matters worse, there is often a fair amount of snow that comes in with the falling skier, as the tree branches unload and snow fills in the void packing around the skier. The person who is upside down is unlikely to be able to pull or dig him or herself out.

Notice that the term for this is snow immersion suffocation – not tree well fatalities? Well, there's a reason for that. Snow immersion suffocations are not limited to tree wells. And Colorado has the unique distinction that eight of the fourteen snow immersion suffocations in the last twenty years did not involve tree wells at all. This is a testament to our state's generally unconsolidated continental snowpack.

Non-tree well related snow immersion suffocations tend to involve falling into snowbanks, falling into snow voids around creek beds, or jumping and then landing into deep snow. The fatalities are almost always a result of the skier falling headfirst, such that the person ends up under the snow in the deadly inverted position.

Experiments have shown that struggling can make a dire situation even worse. Struggling once upside down can cause the snow to pack in and around the skier and compromise his or her airway.

The best way to decrease the risk of a snow immersion suffocation is to always ski with a partner and keep your partner in sight. While this is second nature to experienced backcountry skiers, who tend to follow avalanche protocols and always have a partner, this can be more challenging for in-bound skiers. Forget the old saying that "there are no friends on a powder day." It is safer to ski with a friend on a big powder day, and you are each other's only hope if either of you go under the snow. There is no time to go get help. Remember, if you lose sight of your partner, you could lose your friend.

The keys to avoiding snow immersion suffocation are:

- Don't ski too close to trees.
- Ski with a partner who can pull you out and stay in sight of him or her.
- If you are about to fall while close to a tree, do your best to fall with your skis downhill and with your skis between you and the tree. In other words, as you're falling, do what you can to make sure you are sliding with your skis downhill of your torso, as you do not want to go head-first or upside down into a tree well.
- If you are already falling into the tree well, try to grab onto the tree or tree branches to prevent yourself from falling further into the tree well.

- Carry avalanche equipment (beacon, shovel, and probe). A whistle can be handy to get help from nearby skiers.
- Have the ski area's ski patrol number pre-programmed in your cell phone and get help on the way.
- If digging a friend out of a tree well, dig in towards him or her from the side.
- A quick response is key, so don't go for help – dig your friend out.
- If you're caught in tree well, first and foremost, stay calm. Call for help, and although it may be difficult, slowly and methodically try to extricate yourself. If movement makes the situation worse, stop. Control your breathing and hope your partner kept you in sight.

For more information, see www.deepsnowsafety.org.

Chapter 29

Crevasses, Cornices, and Moats, Oh My!

If not controlled by avalanche professionals, *cornices* can grow above treeline to be far bigger than school buses. They hang over the slopes below, literally suspended in air. As explained in Chapter 19, the mechanisms of wind going over a steep slope creates an eddy on the downwind side (also called the lee side). This eddy drives the snow up into the cornice from below the cornice. As a result, cornices form so that they overhang the snow below them. They demand the utmost respect. Are you really comfortable skiing with a suspended school bus over your head?

Small cornices tend to be less of an issue – except as an avalanche trigger. But a large cornice collapse can be a serious matter. Your ski helmet won't do you any good if a school bus size block of dense snow lands on your head.

While cornices tend to collapse more often during the spring melting cycle, there's no truly safe time under a large cornice. One just plays Russian Roulette when spending time skiing under large cornices. Be aware if there are cornices above – and know the risks you are taking. And, if you are on the top of a ridge – no matter how small – make sure you are not on top of a cornice by accident. While they may be fun to jump off of – unless they're comparatively small – understand that they are risky.

While cornices are a threat in the winter, spring, and early summer, let's move to the risks more likely to be present in the summer and fall. Colorado's glaciers and permanent / semi-permanent snowfields offer their own set of unique dangers.

But first, a word about terminology. Is the tiny permanent snowfield of St. Mary's Glacier really a "glacier?" Or is it just a permanent snowfield? What is a *glacier*, after all? My advice: don't get caught up in definitions. Let's start with a non-glacier example. Below St. Mary's Glacier is the Fall River. Fall River flows into Clear Creek. How can a river be a tributary to a creek? Because no one can precisely define a river or a creek. So, there you go – no one can precisely define a glacier, just like no one can precisely define a river. Indeed, many common definitions of a glacier fall apart quickly. A glacier is not a moving body of snow, because all snow is pulled by gravity downhill. And of course, the downhill creeping snow on my Subaru's windshield, if it's left outside for a few days, does not count as a glacier. Similarly, a glacier is not simply a snowfield with crevasses, because one can find crevasses in non-permanent snowfields. And, not all permanent snowfields have crevasses though the snow does flow downhill. The definition cannot be based on the size of the field or the ice density either, as the Muir Snowfield on Mount Rainier is both much larger and has much denser ice than Colorado's largest glaciers, yet the Muir Snowfield is simply called a snowfield, while everyone calls Arapahoe Glacier and Andrews Glacier, glaciers. Is a glacier defined based upon whether the USGS almost arbitrarily decided to call it a glacier or not on the topographical maps it made many decades ago? That can't be either, as it is hardly fair to call the larger snowfields of Skyscraper Glacier, Montezuma Glacier, and Challenger Glacier only snowfields, while calling St. Mary's Glacier, which is much smaller, a glacier. Heck, the USGS has named and labeled Mills Glacier in Rocky Mountain National Park as a glacier. But Mills Glacier no longer exists (that is, it is no longer permanent).

Look, if a river can flow into a creek, do we really need to define a glacier? If you really need a definition, here is my working definition. A glacier is (i) a permanent snowfield (that is, a snowfield that doesn't disappear in the late summer / early fall), that (ii) people call a glacier with either the official name or local name.

Now that the terminology issue on glaciers is as clear as mud, let's talk about their dangers, as well as the dangers of other permanent snowfields or semi-permanent snowfields.

Snow gets pulled slowly downhill by gravity, and **crevasses** form when the stress of the snow movement overwhelms the snow's cohesion with itself. Alaska, as well as the Pacific Northwest volcanoes, have large glaciers with extraordinary crevasse fields peppered with gigantic crevasses – some big enough to fit a skyscraper into. Colorado's crevasses on the other hand are fairly limited. Setting aside bergschrunds, a particular type of crevasse described below, I've only observed crevasses large enough for someone to fall into on Andrews' Glacier (which I've seen up close) and Arapahoe Glacier (which I've only observed from far away).

On glaciers, often the biggest crevasse is the one right at the top, where the glacier pulls away from the mountain and snow above it. These crevasses are called **bergschrunds**, and I've seen bergschrunds large enough for someone to fall into on Challenger Glacier, Skyscraper Glacier, and Tyndall Glacier. And, they'll occasionally even form in non-permanent snowfields, like King Lake Bowl.

Crevasses and bergschrunds can be a summertime and fall season hazard in Colorado. But the hazard is not nearly as significant as the hazard from crevasses in places like Alaska and the Pacific Northwest Volcanoes. There are few enough crevasses in Colorado, and they tend to be small enough, so it is not common practice in Colorado to rope up on the ascent. Nevertheless, keep your eyes out for them, give them extra space, and don't fall in.

Perhaps a larger danger are **moats**, which are often mistaken for crevasses. And moats are hardly limited to forming on glaciers and permanent snowfields. Rather, many late spring backcountry ski runs will develop moats. While a crevasse is formed by gravity's stress on the snow, a moat is formed by melting from rocks (or occasionally streams). Near many rock walls, or where rocks lurk under a snowfield, moats are formed. Many hikers and skiers on St. Mary's Glacier's edges, especially upper edges, remain blissfully unaware that they are literally standing on snow one foot deep, with five feet of space directly below that snow above the rocks at the bottom. If they paid closer attention to the snow and its edges, they would give moats more space.

I once saw a telemark skier, who was hiking up St. Mary's Glacier with skis on his shoulders, stand too close to the edge of a moat. Before anyone in my group could warn him about his location he disappeared. It literally looked like a magic act where someone disappears right before your eyes. Mystified, I looked down, and the very top of his head was at foot level on the snow as he had just been swallowed up by a moat. We helped him out, and he was fortunately ambulatory enough to return to the trailhead without our assistance. Moats should be given their respect and plenty of space – especially when your skis are not on.

And if we're talking about dangers of summer snow, let's not forget about the fall risk from glacial ice that sometimes becomes exposed later in the summer. And rockfall can certainly be a hazard too. Let's discuss fall risk next.

Chapter 30

Falls / Collisions

In September 1998, two months after last skiing a 45-degree couloir near Tyndall Glacier in Rocky Mountain National Park, I was again skiing the same couloir. The typical route to Tyndall Glacier is to access it from the top – via Flattop Mountain. This is different than many other couloirs, where the common practice is to climb the couloir before skiing it. So, approaching Tyndall Glacier from the top, I didn't know how icy the couloir had become in the last two months.

With my skis on, I started jump turning down the couloir. On the third jump turn, I slipped on the firm old snow and tumbled down the remaining 600 vertical feet to the foot of the glacier. Fortunately, the fall quickly rendered me unconscious, so I remember little of the fall itself. My friend who I was with, and several random hikers in the vicinity, quickly came to my aid. Park rangers, search and rescue, and helicopter teams swung into action. After five hours of going in and out of consciousness at the base of Tyndall Glacier, a helicopter pulled me out and flew me to a hospital. It took a team effort of numerous people to rescue me and save my life, for which I am forever grateful.

I was extraordinarily lucky. I broke eight bones, tore one ligament, and required plastic surgery on my face as my skull was exposed through my forehead and the inside of my mouth was exposed through my chin. That was all the damage. I not only survived but was skiing again late in the year of 1998.

My survival was not guaranteed by any stretch. Ski falls and collisions can be deadly. And they certainly do not have to be as spectacular or as memorable as my long tumble down a steep couloir during the summertime. More people die from collisions with trees on (or just off) intermediate runs at ski areas than die from falls during ski mountaineering. And there are many objects beyond just trees that one can hit while skiing.

It goes without saying that attaching one or two long boards to your feet, and having gravity pull you down a snowy mountainside on those boards, is an inherently risky activity. While most falls are not harmful, falling in the wrong place at the wrong time can literally be deadly.

This is particularly true of collisions. Colliding with something – from another skier to a lift tower – are part of the risks of our sport. Years ago, talking with a helicopter ski guide in British Columbia, I asked him if he had ever had a client die while heli-skiing. The heli-guide responded that he had not, but his closest call was not what one would expect – for example, an avalanche or snow immersion suffocation. Rather, his closest call was from two skiers colliding with each other. This is crazy to think about – a helicopter operation where there is endless space in the wild backcountry, and the most serious accident an experienced guide ever saw dealt with two skiers colliding with each other.

What can you do? It is important to be aware of the dangers of falls and collisions. It is important to not ski too fast. It is important to ski in control. It is important to ski within your own ability. It is important to be able to see where you are headed and be able to avoid people and objects. And, you should wear a helmet.

In case you've forgotten, here is the Skier's Responsibility Code:

1. Always stay in control, and be able to stop or avoid other people or objects.
2. People ahead of you have the right of way. It is your responsibility to avoid them.
3. You must not stop where you obstruct a trail, or are not visible from above.
4. Whenever starting downhill or merging into a trail, look uphill and yield to others.
5. Always use devices to help prevent runaway equipment.

6. Observe all posted signs and warnings. Keep off closed trails and out of closed areas.
7. Prior to using any lift, you must have the knowledge and ability to load, ride and unload safely.

Serious falls and collisions are a danger in skiing. Be careful out there.

Chapter 31

Exposure to the Elements

U nsurprisingly, skiing usually is a cold-season sport, so all the dangers associated with cold temperatures should be kept in mind. These include *hypothermia* (where the body itself gets too cold) and *frostbite* (where skin freezes). Be sure to wear proper clothing when skiing. Layering your clothing is essential – at the end of the day, many skiers feel like they're peeling an onion as they take their layers off. When its cold / windy, do not leave exposed skin. And, head inside if you're getting too cold.

Colorado's mountains are also high. As mentioned in Chapter 2, eight of the ten highest ski areas in North America are in Colorado, with the other two in our sister region of Northern New Mexico.[51] The Imperial Express Superchair at Breckenridge tops out just shy of the summit of Peak 8 at 12,998 feet – the highest ski lift in North America. Indeed, Denver, thousands of feet lower than the lowest Colorado ski area base, is still higher than the summits of ski areas in states such as Alaska or Vermont.

While this means great quality and plentiful snow for Colorado, it also means that visitors must grapple with altitude – including the relatively common *acute mountain sickness*, and occasionally the far more pernicious *high altitude pulmonary edema*. The keys to reducing the likelihood of getting altitude illness include drinking more water, drinking less alcohol (sorry!), and slowly gaining elevation. For visitors to the state, spending a night in

---

[51] There are multiple ways to measure top elevation, so for this statistic I chose the highest lift serviced terrain. If it's the highest lift service *or* hike to terrain, Colorado has nine of the ten highest ski areas in North America.

Denver before heading up to the mountains greatly reduces the likelihood of getting acute mountain sickness. If you're feeling sick, drink more water, descend in elevation, and go to a medical clinic.

Come springtime, *lightning* presents another serious threat. And lightning in Colorado is dangerous. Colorado has the second highest number of lightning fatalities per year on average, coming in second only to far more lightning prone Florida. Lightning is largely absent in the winter because the ground isn't warm enough. Come spring, however, the sun warms the ground which creates warm air. This warm air, coupled with moisture in the air, rises. (Remember, warm air rises – which is why there's no such thing as a cold-air balloon ride.) The rising moist warm air creates thunderheads and an imbalance in electric charges within the thunderhead and between the base of the thunderhead and the ground. This in turn causes lightning. As lightning likes to take the shortest route between the clouds and ground (or vice versa), being on a mountain when there are thunderheads nearby puts you at risk of being struck by lightning. Fortunately, unless mountains block the view, the growth of thunderheads is obvious. It is easy to see their growth and to turn around before they're large enough for a lightning storm to start. Avoid ridges, avoid high points, avoid being above tree-line terrain, avoid being directly under or by trees, and seek shelter when lightning may be imminent.

PART 8

HUNTING THE NON-POWDER JOYS

There's more to life than powder. Perhaps only someone who skis as much powder as I do can say that, but there are so many other joys to skiing than just powder. I can certainly say that the grin on my face is just as large when I'm jump turning down a couloir of velvet corn snow in shorts and a t-shirt in June as it ever is in the deepest of powder conditions.

So, let's finish this book with quick hunting lessons on the three other conditions skiers also love to hunt – fresh groomers, corn snow, and sand.

Chapter 32

Hunting Fresh Groomers

Okay, why are we talking about groomers in a book about finding powder? Because skiing a freshly and perfectly groomed ski run is amazing, if not quite as amazing as skiing deep fresh powder. Just because you love powder, as I do, doesn't mean you can't enjoy a perfectly groomed slope now and again. Wine is my drink of choice, but that doesn't mean I don't also love beer.

In order to find the best groomers, it's helpful to understand some basics of snow grooming. The quality of grooming depends upon four variables: (i) the snow and weather, (ii) the grooming equipment used, (iii) the operator skill, and (iv) overall manpower. Let's address each in turn.

The quality of snow before being groomed has a large impact on the final product of groomed snow. Whether a groomer is working with natural snow or manmade snow makes the biggest difference. One study out of Europe found the surface harness of manmade groomed snow more than twice as hard as that of groomed natural snow. This leads to radically different snow when groomed. Simply, groomed natural snow is far softer than groomed manmade snow. Which one is better? Let me put it this way – when choosing between beers, do you prefer dark ales or IPAs? There's no right or wrong answer, only opinions on which is better. In my opinion soft groomers are better (and dark ales are better), but this is just my opinion. Once you know what you prefer, it's easier to hunt groomers of your choice. But remember, there are many other snow and weather variables. For example, grooming is impacted by new snow, cold temperatures, warm temperatures, and so on and so forth.

The equipment used for grooming matters. As briefly referenced in Chapter 21, when you look at a grooming machine, you'll notice that there is the machine itself, with an attachment on the front and an attachment on the back. If grooming, the grooming machine's front attachment of choice is usually the blade. The blade smooths out irregularities in the slope, flattening and preparing the slope for grooming. The machine itself not only transports the front and rear attachments and the driver, the machine itself also compacts the snow and warms it a bit that helps with grooming. The rear attachment is arguably the most important tool for grooming. The rear attachment is usually a tiller that grinds the snow up, leaving hopefully a wonderfully groomed slope in its wake. The tiller speed, pressure, and cutting angle are all adjustable. More advanced, modern, and expensive tillers (and tiller operators) make for higher quality groomed runs. Sometimes, instead of a tiller, a smoothing board (compactor bar) is used. This heavy attachment just compacts the snow without tilling it – which is a great option for natural snow runs early season, when one doesn't want the tiller to throw up rocks onto the snow surface. Like most technologies, snow grooming equipment is steadily improving, so resorts that invest in top notch equipment tend to have runs that are better groomed. But investing in people is at least as important as investing in equipment.

The skill of the operator of the grooming machine is key. The best operators are artists. Their canvas is the snow they are about to groom. And in the ski industry, the top groomers are as well-known as celebrity chefs are known among the general population. One groomer once bragged to me, and I don't necessarily disbelieve him, that he could shave my face with his grooming machine without leaving a scratch. Ski resorts work hard to find, train, and retain a strong team of grooming machine operators. The better the folks who run grooming machines understand the snow, the terrain, their machine, and the art of grooming – the better the groomed corduroy they create.

Finally, the total amount of human resources a resort is willing to invest makes a big difference in grooming. The timing of grooming is key. While on a majority of nights grooming right after the slopes close is the ideal time, sometimes weather conditions make grooming in the middle of the night or right before opening the best time. Having multiple shifts and flexible schedules helps resorts groom during the ideal time. It also assists when snow conditions warrant more than one pass by the grooming machine, as more people and more time are necessary to cover the terrain to be groomed.

In case it's not clear already, grooming is both an art and a science. How perfectly groomed a slope is depends upon the inputs, the equipment, the operators, and the total manpower.

With this knowledge, how do you find the best groomers? Here are some tips:

Pick up a Grooming Map – The majority of the ski areas in Colorado post a list daily (usually with a map) of which runs are freshly groomed. These maps are amazing and essential in searching out the freshly groomed runs on the mountain. Grab a physical map, or check the map on your phone, and find which runs are freshly groomed that day.

First Tracks (Daytime) – Just like on a fresh powder day, you should try to be in the first group of skiers up the mountain in order to get those first few amazingly fresh groomer runs in. So, aim for first chair. And lift lines for first chair aren't as long as they are on a powder day.

The more people ski a groomed run throughout the day, the less you get that perfect corduroy grooming feel. So, go early, and enjoy those first few runs.

Fancier Resorts – Often times the smaller and less glitzy resorts are the better ones to find the best powder. The opposite rule, however, generally seems to hold true for grooming. Snow is the creation of the heavens. Grooming is the creation of man. And so, resorts with more money can afford fancier grooming machines and can afford to pay groomers to manicure the slopes for more hours each night. So, as a general matter, the fancier the resort, the better the grooming. However, as noted above, so much depends on the operator, I could list several examples of smaller resorts in Colorado that I know who do a better job with grooming than many of the fancier resorts.

Runs Without Snowmaking – Snowmaking machines are wonderful and vital, but as we learned in Chapter 21, to be technical they should be called sleet making machines, not snow making machines. If like me you love soft groomers, the best groomers tend to be on runs where there is no snow-making. But I understand that many smart people disagree – and prefer the harder groomed runs. It's just personal preference.

Snowmaking in Colorado tends to end by late December or early January. So, later in the year natural snowfall makes all runs softer.[52] But earlier in the season, or when there hasn't been fresh snow for a while, how can you figure out which groomed runs have snowmaking snow and which have natural snow? Often, especially early in the season, this is obvious. If it's not obvious, some ski areas put on their trail maps which runs have snowmaking, so you can quickly figure out which groomers are on all-natural snow. And don't forget, even if the ski area trail map doesn't list whether or not the run has snowmaking, if you look for pipes, towers, or other snowmaking apparatus on the sides of runs, that tells you that there is snowmaking on the run.

First Tracks (Nighttime) – Several Colorado ski areas have night skiing, including Echo, Hesperus, Howelsen Hill, Kendall, Keystone, Ski Granby Ranch, and Steamboat. Some of these resorts will re-groom slopes between daytime and nighttime skiing, and there's nothing like getting fresh groomer turns at 5 pm at night. Pay attention to grooming patterns at these hills to figure out when and where to ride freshly groomed runs.

In my humble opinion, perfectly manicured groomed snow cannot beat powder, but it sure still is fun. Let's turn next to the one snow condition that in my mind can rival the best powder.

---

[52] The exception to this rule deals with race courses, where special techniques can harden the snow throughout the ski season.

Chapter 33

Hunting Corn

Ask many a die-hard Colorado backcountry skier what their favorite month for skiing in Colorado is, and more than you'd expect they will respond without hesitation: June. That's certainly my answer.

Why June? Avalanche danger usually (but not always) subsides enough by June to permit skiers to ski Colorado's biggest and craziest lines. The approaches to ski lines can be done in shorts and t-shirts in June. And, Colorado's corn snow has hit its peak.

If you're not familiar with corn snow, it is what many of us refer to as snow groomed by God. Great corn snow is at least as great as the greatest groomed snow. The top inch or two of the snow is slushy, with firm snow underneath permitting perfect carved turns – or crazy jump turns – depending upon where and how you ski.

So, where and how do you find this perfect corn? Let's start with a science lesson. Don't worry, the science is easy.

Where – As spring approaches, the snowpack begins its gradual transformation from midwinter conditions to what scientists call isothermal. Isothermal is just a fancy word for all the same temperature throughout. Midwinter, the snowpack is made up of many layers, all at different temperatures at or below 32 degrees Fahrenheit (0 Celsius). As spring approaches, two key things happen. First, the average temperature – both in the daytime and the nighttime – increases. Second, the sun gets higher in the sky, which causes more heat to enter the snowpack from direct sunlight.

What does this mean? The surface snow begins to melt, and the snowpack becomes more isothermal, based upon three factors. Let's begin by examining two of the three key factors – elevation (i.e., height above sea-level) and aspect (i.e., the direction the snow is facing). Each of these factors are critical. The snowpack at a lower elevation becomes isothermal before the snowpack at higher elevation becomes isothermal. And, south-facing slopes become isothermal before east and west-facing slopes become isothermal, which in turn become isothermal before the north facing slopes become isothermal.

In other words, quality corn first appears at lower elevation south facing slopes, then as the spring season continues, the location of the quality corn snow slowly migrates higher in elevation and to the more northern end of the compass.

While at first blush it may appear that I am talking about the melting pattern, that's not fully accurate. A key portion of melting is depth and density of the snow. A brief example will suffice. The highest elevation and northern most aspect of the entirety of Colorado is the north face of Long's Peak (top elevation 14,259') in Rocky Mountain National Park.[53] Peak baggers know this face as the "cable route," an easy two pitch climb that avoids the more popular "keyhole route." However, due to wind patterns, the depth of snow on this due north portion of Long's Peak, the cable route, is usually mostly melted out by mid-May. On the other hand, a mere four miles to the northwest of Long's Peak is Colorado's second largest glacier, Andrews Glacier. Andrews Glacier (which is formed by the howling west-erly winds of Rocky Mountain National Park) faces east. And, compared to the north face of Long's Peak, the glacier's highest point is at a mere 11,960'. Andrews Glacier, of course, does not melt out before Long's Peak. Rather, its snowfield lasts year-round – and often provides excellent corn ski turns into early August. Elevation and aspect, while two key elements of corn snow, alone are not enough. Snow depth and density must be considered as well – as this is likewise crucial to quality corn snow.

---

[53] While technically Long's Peak is 180' shorter than Colorado's tallest peak, Mt. Elbert, as Long's Peak lies from a latitudinal perspective far to the north, it is fair to characterize it for our purposes as the highest elevation peak in Colorado.

Corn snow tends to be at its best in locations in which the snow is deep. And, indeed, these areas take longer for isothermal conditions to appear due to the depth of the snowpack. Warm temperatures and direct sunlight need more time to convert the entire snowpack to 32 degrees from top to bottom.[54]

So, if you're hunting corn, start the springtime with the lower elevation southern exposures, and as the spring progresses work more northerly and easterly and to higher elevations and deeper snowpacks.

When – The next question in one's quest for perfect corn snow turns, is when the best time is to find it. We've discussed this a bit already, but let's dive in deeper. As the sun rises higher in the sky, occasionally you can find good corn snow in late March, though it's far more common in April than March, and far more common in May than in April. And, the corn appears later as one moves higher in elevation, moves to slopes facing more to the northern areas of the compass, and to a certain extent, to the deeper locations of the snowpack. This means, conversely, that better powder and winter conditions exist during the spring on these higher elevation and more northerly facing areas.

Of course, random snowstorms – very common in March, and still pretty common in April, delay the onset of corn – but who is going to complain about random snowstorms. Snowstorms in May are less common, though occur virtually every year at higher elevations (e.g., over 11,000'). Snowstorms continue into June, but of course less frequently, and even into early July on occasion. The latest I have caught fresh powder was July 3, 2006 on Fourth of July Bowl on Peak 10 above Breckenridge. And although I missed it, the massive July 4, 1995 snowstorm at A-Basin has become a legend. Remember, as discussed in Chapter 23, if you're trying to chase powder in these April and later snowstorms, the sun's position high in the sky will turn the powder into heavy, wet, and unfun skiing quickly. This is often true

---

54   Though technically, the bottom of the snowpack is always at 32 degrees, as described in Chapter 20. A snowpack becomes isothermal as the top and middle layer warm to 32 degrees, to match the bottom layer.

even with clouds. So, be sure to ski the powder as soon as you're able to do so in the morning, before it gets mashed up by the sun.

But when it's not snowing, the corn will come out. And, for above tree-line skiing, corn usually peaks in May and June. And, avalanche risk decreases (but certainly does not disappear) by later in May. In the average Colorado year, quality corn can still be found if you're willing to hike for it, into August.[55]

But it's not just weeks or months one should look at for finding perfect corn, but the time of the day. On the average day in May for any high elevation snow line, the snow will be frozen overnight. It will start the thaw process around 7 am or when the slope first gets sunlight. As the day progresses, the surface snow will become wetter and wetter and slushier and slushier. This means that if you are on the slope too early in the day, the slope will still be icy, which is not good skiing. And icy conditions greatly increase the likelihood of a serious fall. If you are on the slope too late in the day, on the other hand, the slope will be too slushy. Too slushy snow isn't particularly fun to ski, it can make for issues holding a good edge, and the odds of a wet snow avalanche and/or cornice collapse are greater. And, considering that afternoons in Colorado frequently have thunderstorms, one doesn't necessarily want to be on an exposed snow slope at 3 pm in May anyhow.

So, what is the Goldilocks time between too early in the day and too late in the day to ski corn snow? The general rule of thumb in the backcountry is to begin your descent between 10 am and 11 am in the morning. And, I use this rule of thumb not only for May and June, but in July and August

---

[55] While there are locations in other parts of the state that hold snow throughout the summer (for example, Montezuma Glacier and the snowfield (i.e., the Snowmass) above Snowmass Lake), the vast majority of the true summer skiing spots are the series of cirque glaciers and permanent snowfields that line the continental divide from the north end of Rocky Mountain National Park to St. Mary's Glacier. Depending upon the year, many of these snowfields may still have quality corn into early August but one is still taking a bit of a crap shoot to hike several miles in to ski a glacier – whether Andrews, Isabelle, Challenger, or Skyscraper – just to discover that only ice remains and the corn is gone.

too. This timing of course varies upon the aspect – the south facing Christo Couloir on Quandary Peak should be skied earlier as it's south facing, and the west facing snow line on Bald Mountain should be skied later as it doesn't begin to see sun until mid-morning. The timing also varies upon elevation, the quality of the freeze the night before, how sunny it is on the day of the ski, etc. But for a rule of thumb, plan your descent to start between 10 am to 11 am.

Exactly Where – There are so many amazing corn skiing backcountry spots in Colorado, they cannot begin to be summarized in a book like this. However, there are far more guidebooks to spring backcountry skiing in Colorado than winter backcountry skiing. Appendix F lists many of these books, so buy a couple of these books to figure out where to go. Or just pay attention as you drive around the mountains of Colorado in the spring and early summer to see where the snow looks the best. I've found many great corn lines simply doing this. Enjoy.

Chapter 34

Hunting Sand

W hy restrict your skiing just to snow? My daughter began learning to ski at Shredders in Boulder – an indoor facility where children are taught how to ski without dealing with the elements – on slopes made of Xtreme – the skiing equivalent of AstroTurf. Skis slide on many surfaces. But the pinnacle of all non-snow surfaces on which skis glide is sand.

One who doesn't know Colorado well may first think – Colorado cannot possibly be a good location for sand skiing as there are no beaches. Well think again. The tallest sand dunes in North America (up to almost 700' tall) are in Colorado. Great Sand Dunes National Park and Preserve in the Sangre de Christo Mountain Range in southern Colorado offers probably the best sand skiing in North America – with 500-foot vertical of consistent pitch dune skiing.

For those readers who have never skied sand – you should definitely do it.

Where to Go – The Great Sand Dunes National Park and Preserve is a four-hour drive south-southwest of Denver, with camping options both within and outside of the national park. Technically you can ski anywhere on any dune in the national park, as the wind re-blows the sand every night making it pristine for the next morning. While there are places you can ski out from the main paved parking lot past the visitor's center, it's usually not worth skiing out of this area. There is a long flat section to cross by Medano Creek (often dry in the fall) when headed out from this trailhead, and the dunes only rise slowly from that point.

The better skiing option, and the far more popular ski spot, are the dunes a little north of the visitor center, at the Castle Creek picnic area. Depending upon the road conditions on any particular day, the road (Medano Pass Primitive Road) to Castle Creek requires quality AWD or 4WD. And, the best way to drive up this road often involves dropping your tire pressure to 20 psi for better grip on the sandy road. The park has a free air pump available to refill tires when coming back onto pavement. Obviously please follow the national park's recommendations on proper vehicles, but for what it's worth, I've never failed to make it to Castle Creek in a Subaru.

Once at Castle Creek, you walk across the small creek (often dry in the fall) and a large tall dune is directly ahead of you. Climbing or skinning is easiest to the climber's left side of the dune, with the descent straight above the trailhead from the highest spot. You can put in beautiful tracks straight back to the creek, with your car only a stone's throw away. And, in-spite of the ever slightly shifting dune patterns, this dune remains fairly consistently at the maximum steepness of sand, 34 degrees. It's been consistent since I started skiing it over two decades ago.

When to Go – While skiing on the dunes is possible year-round – winter makes little sense as there's tons of great snow skiing elsewhere. And, the heart of summer can be difficult simply due to the hot days on the dunes. My vote for the best time of year is late spring or early fall, when it's neither too cold nor too hot at the dunes, and the summer crowds are not too crazy. Considering all the great spring skiing in Colorado, I tend to go to the dunes in the early fall. What a better way to ski in September than to ski on sand?

What Gear to Bring – Don't bring your brand-new skis and bindings to the dunes – sand gets everywhere and isn't very good for bindings. An older / cheaper pair of skis will do the trick, though smooth bases are helpful. Do not bring skins. Water and sunscreen on sand dunes is important. (Duh – you're skiing on Colorado's equivalent of the Sahara Desert.) Some people bring lemon-scented pledge to spray on the bottom of their skis allegedly for faster skiing – though the park service frowns on this practice. Some local shops sell sand wax. I've had mixed experiences with this wax. Good eyewear is important — whether wrap-around sunglasses or goggles, as sand in the eyes is never a good thing. (I can attest from personal experience on that one.) And, if you're hiking as opposed to skinning, a comfy backpack to hold skis is important as it's a real hike up. And, make sure your footwear is adequate if you're not wearing ski boots — as the sand gets hot!

How to Go Up – There are no ski lifts and driving on the dunes is not permitted, so you'll have to hike or skin up to the top of the sand dune. But, the run down is well worth it.

Hiking up with skis or a snowboard on your back is always a fine option, though as one would expect with sand, it's one step up, a half a step slide back. The better option for those with AT / Tele / Split-board gear is to skin up, but without skins. Sand holds to about a 15-degree angle uphill, so you can usually skin up without skins if you have the right bindings.

Whether you hike or skin, don't head straight up the dunes by Castle Creek. It's too consistently steep to be a pleasant ascent. Rather, go up on the climber's left side where the slopes are gentler.

What the Ski Down is Like – Skiing on sand is usually like skiing on perfectly groomed snow, with two major exceptions. First, it's much noisier as the heavy sand is pushed ever so slightly by your skis. Second, and more important, the dunes ski as if they're gentler than the equivalent pitch of snow. The maximum angle sand holds is 34 degrees, which is usually the angle of the main pitch of Castle Creek. While this is an angle of a steeper black diamond run on snow, on sand it skis more like an easy blue square. For those comfortable with snow angles, just subtract roughly 15 degrees from the snow angle to get the equivalent sand angle — so the main pitch skis like 19 degrees, even though it's 34 degrees. This leads to the odd sensation of feeling like you are leaning forwards like it's a steep black diamond, while the turns feel like an easy blue. This can take some getting used to.

A few additional tips on skiing sand. As hard as my friends and I have tried, it's nearly impossible to build a jump out of sand. The small jumps we built weren't much fun anyhow, so it's not worth your time trying. And, straight-lining doesn't get you going much faster, so sticking with gentle carved turns is far more fun than trying to get aggressive. Also, please be cognizant of sand dune dangers. Make sure you have adequate footwear, eyewear, and water. Heat can be an issue. Obviously, lighting is a risk, and indeed every time you see black sand on the dunes, that black sand is a result of the lightning hitting the sand.

So, grab your old skis and head to the dunes! Do you really have better plans for this weekend than skiing on sand?

Parting Thoughts and Going Beyond Colorado

Now that we're almost at the end of the book – except for lots of appendices and a hopefully enlightening and entertaining glossary – let's take a brief look at what we've discussed in this book. Weather is complicated. It is a true four-dimensional system – with differences of air and water vapor in three dimensions of space, and always in motion.

Predicting weather is even more complicated than understanding weather. While human knowledge and computing power is making weather prediction constantly better, the chaos of the weather system prevents the ability to ever have perfect forecasts.

Predicting powder is even more complicated than predicting most other types of weather. Heck, even once snow has fallen it's difficult to say exactly how much has fallen. So, it is quite a trick to predict something when we don't even fully know the end result.

But let's not be pessimistic. Understanding a little about meteorology and climatology can go a long way to making better predictions of where and when to find powder. We don't need perfect predictions for powder skiing, so long as we're making better predictions for powder than just the historical average. To use a gambling analogy, you don't have to win every hand. You just want to be able to beat the house. With a basic grasp of meteorology and Colorado's climatology, you hopefully now should have a better understanding of where it snows, when it snows, and why it snows. This should help you make better choices of when and where to ski.

And, while this book is just about Colorado, it should be noted that you've learned powder hunting tools that will help you in most mountains throughout the world. Starting closest to home, if you look at a satellite image map of the Colorado Rocky Mountains, you'll quickly notice that the same mountain chains runs south into northern New Mexico, and north just a touch into Wyoming. Our mountain range really runs from Snowy Range Ski Area, Wyoming (in the north) to Ski Santa Fe, New Mexico (in the south); and from Powderhorn (in the west) to Echo Mountain (in the east).

Northern New Mexico sees virtually the same snow patterns as the rest of Colorado, and every word of this book is equally applicable to northern New Mexico. The same is true for a small swath of mountains in Wyoming. Mountains do not recognize state lines. It almost seems unfair to leave the northern New Mexico ski areas (Angel Fire, Pajarito Mountain, Red River, Ski Santa Fe, Sipapu Ski Resort, and Taos Ski Valley); and Wyoming's Snowy Range out of Appendix A, simply because of where the state line is located.

While the patterns may not be quite the same as we get further away from Colorado's mountains – into Utah, the rest of Wyoming, Montana, etc., the same general rules and meteorological principals apply. You should read more on maritime snow and lake effect snow, but otherwise this book has covered most of the powder basics. Orographic lifting works the same way everywhere – whether you're skiing in Colorado or the Snowy Mountains of Australia.

For Colorado skiers, it's easy to forget there is a whole world of powder skiing out there beyond Colorado; when in our backyard are ski areas like Aspen and Vail, and backcountry areas like Berthoud Pass and Red Mountain Pass. But there is an entire world of incredible skiing beyond the four corners of our state. Ski Alaska. Ski Japan. Ski the Alps. Ski Utah. Ski anywhere and everywhere.

I hope this book has helped in your quest to find more powder.

And, I hope this book has been as fun for you to read as it was for me to write. If I run into you in the mountains, I hope we can see each other's grins, but only barely see each other's grins, through all the powder snow from so many face shots. Happy powder hunting!

Appendix A

Where to Chase Powder Location by Location

From legendary ski resorts like Aspen and Breckenridge, to largely unknown outside of Colorado gems like Monarch and Sunlight, Colorado has every size and type of ski resort imaginable. This appendix presents the basic information on each ski area in Colorado – from the giant and famous Vail to the no ticket, no lodge, single rope tow Lee's Ski Hill. (In other words, if it has a lift and is open for the public to ski, it is listed in this appendix.)[56]

As this is a book about skiing Colorado, the northern New Mexico ski areas are not included, but it should be remembered that if it weren't for the state line, they would fit right in with Colorado snow. The same is true for Snowy Range in southern Wyoming. Snowfall, vertical, and acreage information for these resorts is set forth in the footnote.[57]

---

[56] I've only listed ski areas with lifts, but folks should not forget Bluebird Backcountry, an inbounds backcountry ski area near Kremmling, Colorado. https://bluebirdbackcountry.com/.

[57] Here are the stats:
Angel Fire Resort, NM: Snowfall is 210", Vertical is 2,077', Acreage is 560 acres.
Pajarito Mountain, NM: Snowfall is n/a, Vertical is 1,440', Acreage is 750 acres
Red River, NM: Snowfall is 214", Vertical is 1,600', Acreage is 209 acres.
Ski Santa Fe, NM: Snowfall is 225", Vertical is 1,725', Acreage is 660 acres.
Sipapu Ski Resort, NM: Snowfall is 190", Vertical is 1,055', Acreage is 200 acres.
Snowy Range, WY: Snowfall is 245"; Vertical is 865', Acreage is 250 acres.
Taos Ski Valley, NM: Snowfall is 300"; Vertical is 3,281', Acreage is 1,295 acres.

As for the 33 Colorado Ski Areas, the information I provide on each ski area, where available, are:

- The ski area's name;
- The ski area's website;
- The nearest town to the ski area;
- The total skiable acreage;
- The total acres covered by snowmaking;
- The top elevation;
- The vertical drop (i.e., the difference between the top elevation and the base elevation);
- The typical ski season (i.e., opening to closing);
- The favored wind directions for snowfall;
- The nearest University of Utah NAEFS Downscale Model (see Chapter 12 on this forecasting tool);
- The main orientation of the ski area (i.e., north, west, etc.);
- The average annual snowfall (per the resorts website and/or Colorado Ski Country USA);
- The ZRankings average annual snowfall (zrankings.com's estimate);
- Nearby Cat Skiing and/or Helicopter Skiing Operations;
- Popular nearby backcountry skiing locations with similar snow conditions / snowfall patterns; and
- My brief description of each ski area's powder potential.

Getting reliable data for this appendix is always a challenge. This is especially true for annual snowfall. Much of Chapter 18 was spent on the challenges of measuring snowfall – and that no snowfall measurement is ever, or can ever be, completely accurate. No data, when it comes to snowfall, is perfect. Fortunately for the sake of our data, the differences year-to-year and day-to-day in snowfall make slight inaccuracies in the multi-decade averages I use not seem too important. Which is important to note – snowfall numbers are averages and can vary widely. For example, the worst winter at Berthoud Pass in the last forty years – winter 2001-2002, had roughly 35% of the total snow than the best winter in the last forty years – winter 2010-2011. So,

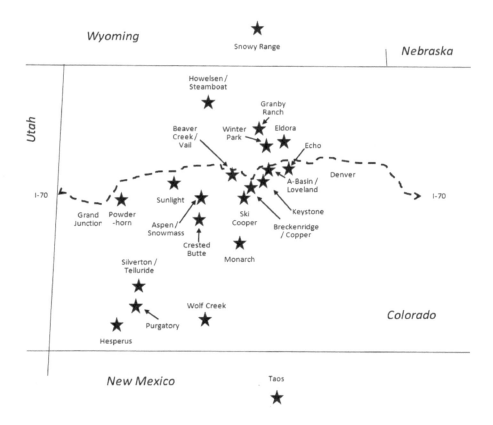

much like weather forecasts, multi-decade analyses of snowfall are helpful in figuring out where and when to ski, but do not guarantee new snow on any particular day or week. Mother nature likes to be unpredictable.

So, how does this appendix pull together data? For the basic infor-mation − elevation, vertical,[58] total acreage, snowmaking acreage, ski sea-

---

[58] Unlike some of these other pieces of information, top elevation and vertical requires a quick clarification. Top elevation is the top elevation whether by lift or by hiking within the resort. The same is true for vertical drop. So, the vertical drop of Snowmass runs from the top of its Cirque lift (at 12,510') to the base of the Two Creeks lift (at 8,110'). Similarly, the vertical drop of Telluride is virtually the same, running from the top of the Palmyra Peak (13,150') to the

son, and snowfall, I rely upon the ski resort's website and/or Colorado Ski Country USA's data. When neither is available, I rely upon onthesnow.com. As one always wants a second opinion when it comes to snowfall numbers, I also provide zrankings.com snowfall total, when available. I have not independently verified any of these numbers, and as this book was written over a period of years, some of the numbers may also be slightly out-of-date. Take all the numbers with a grain of salt, and my apologies for any errors.

There are a few other categories that have been handcrafted for this appendix. With regards to favored wind direction, this is my subjective sense of which wind directions produce the most snow. It is based upon my personal experience, watching forecasts, reviewing meteorological literature, reading forecaster's comments, and often discussing the issue with locals I know in the areas. In other words, this favored wind direction is from an amalgamation of sources, and it has not been scientifically assembled. As such, the favored wind direction comments are my subjective thoughts – so take them for what they are worth. The only exceptions are Crested Butte and Monarch, for which I was able to find published literature with real multi-year data.

And to be fully transparent, Joel Gratz strongly disagreed with a good number of my thoughts. Do you want a more definitive answer to the best wind directions for snow at each of Colorado's ski resorts? Well, hopefully for the 2021-2022 ski season, this information (as well as a digital version of this book) will be available on the All-Access subscription from Open Snow.

As for the main orientation of the ski area, this is my personal assessment based upon having a feel for every ski area in the state. Obviously, ski areas have terrain facing in every direction – but I've chosen the most common direction. For example, while Vail's back bowls tend to be south facing, but as the front side of Vail and Vail's Blue Sky Basin tend to be north facing, I classify Vail's main orientation as north.

---

base of the Coonskin lift (8,725'). To get to Palmyra Peak requires a serious hike, however, as the top of the highest lift at Telluride is 12,515'. Telluride's lift-served vertical drop is over 600' less than Snowmass, but the numbers in the appendix include hike-to-terrain.

Finally, while this appendix is only categorized by ski areas, we shouldn't forget about cat skiing operations, heli skiing operations, and backcountry skiing. This appendix provides information on nearby cat skiing and helicopter skiing operations, if any. As I have not skied many of these operations, please note that this information is not as complete as the ski area list. And, research cat skiing before you do it – as some operations are full day operations in large backcountry areas, while other ones are simply a quick cat ride within the bounds of the ski area that only makes the hike-to-terrain easier to access.

The appendix also provides a brief list of popular backcountry locations that see similar snow patterns to the ski areas listed. The similar backcountry terrain list is based upon my personal experience. It is subjective, and it also has a bias towards providing information on the backcountry terrain I frequently ski (which tends to be closer to the Front Range). So, while I suspect that Coal Bank Pass snow conditions are similar to Purgatory and Molas Pass conditions are similar to Silverton, as I (embarrassingly) have not skied either pass, I leave this information out. Also, it should be noted that no ski area has similar snow conditions to the popular backcountry spot Cameron Pass. I think the best way to view Cameron Pass's snow conditions is as an amalgamation of snow conditions at Eldora, Loveland, and Steamboat. And, I should note that the University of Utah has an NAEFS Downscaled Ensemble Model for Cameron Pass.

With that background, here we go:

Name:	**Arapahoe Basin** (a/k/a A-Basin)
Website:	arapahoebasin.com
Nearest City:	Keystone
Ski Area Information:	
Total Acreage:	1,428 acres
Snowmaking Acreage:	125 acres
Top Elevation:	13,050'
Vertical Drop:	2,530'
Typical Ski Season:	Mid-October to Early June

Favored Wind Directions for Snowfall:	West, Northwest (also southwest and east)
Nearby Univ. Utah NAEFS Downscale:	Tunnel E Portal, CO
Main Orientation:	North
Average Annual Snowfall:	350"
ZRankings Average Annual Snowfall:	314"
Nearby Cat Skiing Operations:	At Keystone and Loveland ski areas
Popular Backcountry with Similar Snow:	Loveland Pass

Arapahoe Basin is a primarily a local's mountain, and it is popular with locals for good reason. It boasts Colorado's longest ski season, and it is well known for some of the most challenging terrain near the Front Range.

Name:	**Aspen Highlands**
Website:	www.aspensnowmass.com
Nearest City:	Aspen
Ski Area Information:	
Acreage:	1,040 acres
Snowmaking acreage:	121 acres
Top Elevation:	12,392'
Vertical Drop:	3,365'
Typical Ski Season:	mid-December to early April
Favored Wind Directions for Snowfall:	West (also northwest and southwest)
Nearby Univ. Utah NAEFS Downscale:	Aspen Airport, CO
Main Orientation:	Northeast
Average Annual Snowfall:	300"
ZRankings Average Annual Snowfall:	252"

Nearby Cat Skiing Operations: At the resort

Popular Backcountry with Similar   Alfred Braun Hut System,

Snow: Independence Pass

Aspen Highlands is known as the steepest of the Aspen ski areas. It is practically impossible to call yourself a true Colorado skier until you've hiked up the famous Highland Bowl and then descended one of its steep and comparatively untracked lines.

Name:	**Aspen Mountain**
Website:	www.aspensnowmass.com
Nearest City:	Aspen
Ski Area Information:	
Acreage:	675 acres
Snowmaking acreage:	210 acres
Top Elevation:	11,212'
Vertical Drop:	3,267'
Typical Ski Season:	Late November to mid-April
Favored Wind Directions for Snowfall:	West (also northwest and southwest)
Nearby Univ. Utah NAEFS Downscale:	Aspen Airport, CO
Main Orientation:	North
Average Annual Snowfall:	300"
ZRankings Average Annual Snowfall:	250"
Nearby Cat Skiing Operations:	At the resort (Aspen Powder Tours)
Popular Backcountry with Similar Snow:	Alfred Braun Hut System, Independence Pass

Aspen Mountain is one of the most famous Colorado ski resorts. It is the named location for many movies from Dumb & Dumber to Aspen Extreme. Its long steep face and outstanding views make its fame well deserved.

Name:	**Beaver Creek**
Website:	Beavercreek.com
Nearest City:	Beaver Creek / Avon
Ski Area Information:	
Acreage:	1,832 acres
Snowmaking acreage:	650 acres
Top Elevation:	11,440'
Vertical Drop:	3,340'
Typical Ski Season:	Late November to mid-April
Favored Wind Directions for Snowfall:	West (also southwest, northwest)
Nearby Univ. Utah NAEFS Downscale:	Vail Pass, CO
Main Orientation:	North
Average Annual Snowfall:	325"
ZRankings Average Annual Snowfall:	325"

I have many friends who list Beaver Creek as their favorite resort in the state (and a few who list it as their favorite resort in the world). Top notch grooming, fewer crowds than nearby Vail, and free cookies at the end of the day make Beaver Creek one of the most beloved large resorts in Colorado.

Name:	**Breckenridge**
Website:	Breckenridge.com
Nearest City:	Breckenridge
Ski Area Information:	
Acreage:	2,908 acres
Snowmaking acreage:	657 acres
Top Elevation:	12,998'
Vertical Drop:	3,398'
Typical Ski Season:	Early November to late April

Favored Wind Directions for Snowfall:	West (also southwest, northwest)
Nearby Univ. Utah NAEFS Downscale:	Tunnel E Portal, CO or Vail Pass, CO
Main Orientation:	Northeast
Average Annual Snowfall:	353"
ZRankings Average Annual Snowfall:	282"
Popular Backcountry with Similar Snow:	Bald Mountain, Hoosier Pass

Breckenridge has the highest lift in North America, the detachable quad Imperial Express Super Chair. The Imperial Express is the only chairlift in Colorado that is entirely above treeline.[59] While Breckenridge has extraordinary quantities of easier terrain, it is best known by powder hounds for its high alpine terrain.

Name:	**Buttermilk**
Website:	www.aspensnowmass.com
Nearest City:	Aspen
Ski Area Information:	
Acreage:	470 acres
Snowmaking acreage:	108 acres
Top Elevation:	9,900'
Vertical Drop:	2,030'
Typical Ski Season:	early-December to early-April
Favored Wind Directions for Snowfall:	West (also northwest and southwest)
Nearby Univ. Utah NAEFS Downscale:	Aspen Airport, CO

---

[59] The Revelation lift at Telluride is awfully close to being completely above treeline, with just a small group of trees a bit of the way up. And, there are a handful of surface lifts that are entirely above treeline.

Main Orientation:	Northeast
Average Annual Snowfall:	200"
ZRankings Average Annual Snowfall:	200"
Nearby Cat Skiing Operations:	At Aspen Mountain and Aspen Highlands

Buttermilk holds the dual identity of being one of the great beginner mountains in the United States while simultaneously hosting the X-Games. While the great skiers in the Aspen area flock to the other three mountains, Buttermilk for that very reason often holds powder for quite some time.

Name:	**Chapman Hill**
Website:	http://co-durango.civicplus.com/544/Ski-Hill
Nearest City:	Durango
Ski Area Information:	
Acreage:	7 acres
Snowmaking acreage:	7 acres
Top Elevation:	6,840'
Vertical Drop:	280'
Typical Ski Season:	mid-December to mid-March
Favored Wind Directions for Snowfall:	n/a
Nearby Univ. Utah NAEFS Downscale:	Durango Airport, CO
Main Orientation:	North
Average Annual Snowfall:	n/a
Nearby Cat Skiing Operations:	At Purgatory

Chapman Hill is the Durango town ski hill with a short beginner rope tow and a longer intermediate rope tow. It's a cute place to visit, but not a spot for powder skiing.

Name:	**Copper Mountain**
Website:	coppercolorado.com
Nearest City:	Copper
Ski Area Information:	
Acreage:	2,527 acres
Snowmaking Acreage:	364 acres
Top Elevation:	12,313'
Vertical Drop:	2,601'
Typical Ski Season:	early November to late April
Favored Wind Directions for Snowfall:	West (also southwest, northwest)
Nearby Univ. Utah NAEFS Downscale:	Vail Pass, CO
Main Orientation:	North
Average Annual Snowfall:	306"
ZRankings Average Annual Snowfall:	278"
Nearby Cat Skiing Operations:	Vail Powder Guides
Popular Backcountry with Similar Snow:	Fremont Pass, Mayflower Gulch

Copper Mountain has above treeline terrain facing in every compass direction, and below treeline the mountain naturally separates the terrain between beginners, intermediates, and experts. This leads to many excellent powder chasing options.

Name:	**Cranor Hill**
Website:	http://www.gunnisonco.gov/departments/parks_and_recreation/cranor_ski_area.php
Nearest City:	Gunnison
Ski Area Information:	

Acreage:	45 acres
Snowmaking acreage:	None
Top Elevation:	8,320'
Vertical Drop:	650'
Typical Ski Season:	January to March
Favored Wind Directions for Snowfall:	Northwest
Nearby Univ. Utah NAEFS Downscale:	Gunnison Airport, CO
Main Orientation:	Northeast
Average Annual Snowfall:	n/a
Nearby Cat Skiing Operations:	Irwin Guides

With one poma lift climbing a 650' hill without a single tree on the hill makes for an unusual sight, but powder is not unheard of on this small no snowmaking ski area on the road to Crested Butte.

Name:	**Crested Butte**
Website:	skicb.com
Nearest City:	Crested Butte
Ski Area Information:	
Acreage:	1,547 acres
Snowmaking acreage:	297 acres
Top Elevation:	12,162'
Vertical Drop:	3,062'
Typical Ski Season:	Late November to early April
Favored Wind Directions for Snowfall:	West (also southwest, northwest, and north)
Nearby Univ. Utah NAEFS Downscale:	Crested Butte-Banana, CO
Main Orientation:	North
Average Annual Snowfall:	234"

ZRankings Average Annual Snowfall:	253"
Nearby Cat Skiing Operations:	Irwin Guides
Popular Backcountry with Similar Snow:	Red Lady

Crested Butte is legendary for its double-diamond terrain. Cliffs, chutes, steeps, and trees all abound on this wild mountain. That said, it does have some groomers too. And, certain storms seem to hit Crested Butte and only Crested Butte. So, some powder days it's the best place to be in the entire state.

Name:	**Echo Mountain**
Website:	www.echomountainresort.com
Nearest City:	Evergreen
Ski Area Information:	
Acreage:	60 acres
Snowmaking Acreage:	40 acres
Top Elevation:	10,650'
Vertical Drop:	600'
Typical Ski Season:	mid-November to mid-April
Favored Wind Directions for Snowfall:	East (also southeast, northeast, and northwest)
Nearby Univ. Utah NAEFS Downscale:	n/a
Main Orientation:	North
Average Annual Snowfall:	275"

Echo Mountain is the closest resort to Denver, which means that it sits in a prime location for upslope storms. If it's snowing lightly in Denver, then it's probably storming like mad at Echo Mountain.

Name:	**Eldora**
Website:	www.eldora.com
Nearest City:	Nederland
Ski Area Information:	
Acreage:	680 acres
Snowmaking acreage:	612 acres
Top Elevation:	10,600'
Vertical Drop:	1,400'
Typical Ski Season:	mid-November to mid-April
Favored Wind Directions for Snowfall:	East (also southeast, northeast, west)
Nearby Univ. Utah NAEFS Downscale:	n/a
Main Orientation:	Northeast
Average Annual Snowfall:	300"
ZRankings Average Annual Snowfall:	225"
Popular Backcountry with Similar Snow:	St. Mary's Glacier, Indian Peaks, Rocky Mountain National Park (Hidden Valley, Bear Lake)

Eldora is the biggest ski area well to the east of the continental divide, which means that it gets hammered in upslope storms. So, if the wind is blowing from the eastern side of the compass, you will not find a better ski area for fresh powder.

Name:	**Frisco Adventure Park**
Website:	https://www.townoffrisco.com/ play/winter-tubing-skiing/tubing/
Nearest City:	Frisco
Ski Area Information:	
Acreage:	n/a
Snowmaking acreage:	n/a
Top Elevation:	9,160'

Vertical Drop:	n/a
Typical Ski Season:	early January to early April
Favored Wind Directions for Snowfall:	n/a
Nearby Univ. Utah NAEFS Downscale:	n/a
Main Orientation:	Northwest
Average Annual Snowfall:	n/a
Nearby Cat/Heli Skiing Operations:	At Keystone and Copper Mountain

Frisco Adventure Park has a couple of short ski runs accessed by the same conveyor lift that services its (more popular) tubing hill. As it's technically a ski area, it's included in this list only for the sake of completeness. Not a place for powder.

Name:	**Granby Ranch**
Website:	granbyranch.com
Nearest City:	Granby
Ski Area Information:	
Acreage:	406 acres
Snowmaking acreage:	65 acres
Top Elevation:	9,202'
Vertical Drop:	1000'
Typical Ski Season:	mid-December to late-March
Favored Wind Directions for Snowfall:	Northwest (also west)
Nearby Univ. Utah NAEFS Downscale:	n/a
Main Orientation:	North
Average Annual Snowfall:	120"
ZRankings Average Annual Snowfall:	200"

| Nearby Cat/Heli Skiing Operations: | At Winter Park |

Although not as big as its Grand County neighbor of Winter Park, Granby Ranch is a well-laid out family mountain that affords plenty of spots to find powder – especially as many of the powder skiers head to Winter Park instead.

Name:	**Hesperus**
Website:	ski-hesperus.com
Nearest City:	Hesperus
Ski Area Information:	
Acreage:	60 acres
Snowmaking acreage:	None
Top Elevation:	8,888'
Vertical Drop:	788'
Typical Ski Season:	mid-December to mid-March
Favored Wind Directions for Snowfall:	Southwest (also west and south)
Nearby Univ. Utah NAEFS Downscale:	Durango Airport, CO
Main Orientation:	Northeast
Average Annual Snowfall:	150"
Nearby Cat Skiing Operations:	At Purgatory

Hesperus, a short drive from Durango, is on a mountainside with few trees. It has lots of spots to find powder from its sole double chair lift. And, with an afternoon storm, you can chase powder into the evening under its lights.

Name:	**Howelsen Hill**
Website:	steamboatsprings.net/131/ Howelsen-Hill-Ski-Area
Nearest City:	Steamboat Springs

Ski Area Information:

Acreage:	50 acres
Snowmaking acreage:	50 acres
Top Elevation:	7,136'
Vertical Drop:	440'
Typical Ski Season:	late-November to early-March
Favored Wind Directions for Snowfall:	West (also southwest and northwest)
Nearby Univ. Utah NAEFS Downscale:	Steamboat Springs Airport, CO
Main Orientation:	Northeast
Average Annual Snowfall:	170"
Nearby Cat Skiing Operations:	Steamboat Powder Cats

Howelsen Hill is the only town operated hill in Colorado that I've had truly great powder days at. While it is known more as a ski jumping and ski racing hill, it is sufficiently wide, long, and steep to provide multiple powder stashes.

Name:	**Kendall Mountain**
Website:	https://www.colorado.gov/pacific/townofsilverton/ski-kendall
Nearest City:	Silverton

Ski Area Information:

Acreage:	16 acres
Snowmaking acreage:	None
Top Elevation:	9,596'
Vertical Drop:	283'
Typical Ski Season:	mid-December to late March
Favored Wind Directions for Snowfall:	n/a
Nearby Univ. Utah NAEFS Downscale:	Coal Bank Pass, CO

Main Orientation:	Northwest
Average Annual Snowfall:	200"
Nearby Heli Skiing Operations:	At Silverton

Kendall Mountain is the town hill for Silverton with one double chair-lift and a handful of runs. It's cute, but don't expect much powder skiing.

Name:	**Keystone**
Website:	keystoneresort.com
Nearest City:	Keystone
Ski Area Information:	
Acreage:	3,148 acres
Snowmaking acreage:	662 acres
Top Elevation:	12,408'
Vertical Drop:	3,128'
Typical Ski Season:	late-October to early April
Favored Wind Directions for Snowfall:	West (also southwest and northwest)
Nearby Univ. Utah NAEFS Downscale:	Tunnel E Portal, CO
Main Orientation:	North
Average Annual Snowfall:	235"
ZRankings Average Annual Snowfall:	235"
Nearby Cat Skiing Operations:	At the resort
Popular Backcountry with Similar Snow:	Montezuma

Keystone Mountain is a large ski area covering three mountains – with runs and trees on many aspects, many elevations, and many terrain features. What does this mean? Many possibilities of finding powder stashes.

Name:	**Lake City**
Website:	http://www.townoflakecity.co/ lake-city-ski-hill.html
Nearest City:	Lake City
Ski Area Information:	
Acreage:	14 acres
Snowmaking acreage:	None
Top Elevation:	9,100'
Vertical Drop:	247'
Typical Ski Season:	December to March
Favored Wind Directions for Snowfall:	n/a
Nearby Univ. Utah NAEFS Downscale:	n/a
Main Orientation:	Northeast
Average Annual Snowfall:	n/a

With one poma lift on a 250' vertical side of a mountain, Lake City is one of the smallest ski areas in Colorado. However, Lake City provides multiple runs from beginner to advanced from this one lift, and powder in the trees is certainly not unheard of.

Name:	**Lee's Ski Hill**
Website:	http://www.ci.ouray.co.us/city_offices/ city_resources/lee_s_ski_hill.php
Nearest City:	Ouray
Ski Area Information:	
Acreage:	n/a
Snowmaking acreage:	None
Top Elevation:	7,792'
Vertical Drop:	75'
Typical Ski Season:	late-December to early March

Favored Wind Directions for Snowfall:	n/a
Nearby Univ. Utah NAEFS Downscale:	Red Mt Pass, CO
Main Orientation:	North
Average Annual Snowfall:	n/a
Nearby Heli Skiing Operations:	At Silverton Mountain

Lee's Ski Hill is Colorado's smallest ski area, and it's one of a kind. No tickets, no lodge, no snowmaking, no grooming. Just one rope tow covering half a city block, open on weekends and after school snow permitting. While it may not be a spot for powder skiing, if you're driving through Ouray with skis in your car, you have to do a few laps for the novelty.

Name:	**Loveland**
Website:	skiloveland.com
Nearest City:	Dillon
Ski Area Information:	
Acreage:	1,800 acres
Snowmaking acreage:	240 acres
Top Elevation:	13,010'
Vertical Drop:	2,210'
Typical Ski Season:	mid–October to early May
Favored Wind Directions for Snowfall:	West (also northwest, east, southeast)
Nearby Univ. Utah NAEFS Downscale:	Tunnel E Portal, CO
Main Orientation:	East
Average Annual Snowfall:	422"
ZRankings Average Annual Snowfall:	344"

Nearby Cat Skiing Operations:	Powder Addiction and at the resort
Popular Backcountry with Similar Snow:	Loveland Pass, Dry Gulch, Jones Pass, Butler Gulch

At the top of the continental divide, Loveland gets hammered from storms coming from the west. And, Loveland gets hammered from storms coming from the east. Add the fact that it is one of the closest ski areas to Denver and has the second highest chairlift in North America, it's no wonder this local resort is known for its powder.

Name:	**Monarch Mountain**
Website:	skimonarch.com
Nearest City:	Salida
Ski Area Information:	
Acreage:	800 acres
Snowmaking acreage:	None
Top Elevation:	11,952'
Vertical Drop:	1,162'
Typical Ski Season:	Late November to early April
Favored Wind Directions for Snowfall:	East (also southeast, south, and west)
Nearby Univ. Utah NAEFS Downscale:	Monarch Pass, CO
Main Orientation:	East
Average Annual Snowfall:	350"
ZRankings Average Annual Snowfall:	284"
Nearby Cat Skiing Operations:	At the resort
Popular Backcountry with Similar Snow:	Monarch Pass

Imagine a high-elevation mountain straddling the continental divide, sufficiently far from Denver to not see big crowds, and with a completely natural snow base. Although not a giant resort, Monarch is well known as a fantastic spot for powder skiing.

Name:	**Powderhorn**
Website:	powderhorn.com
Nearest City:	Mesa
Ski Area Information:	
Acreage:	1,600 acres
Snowmaking Acreage:	42 acres
Top Elevation:	9,850'
Vertical Drop:	1,650'
Typical Ski Season:	mid-December to late-March
Favored Wind Directions for Snowfall:	West (also southwest, northwest, and north)
Nearby Univ. Utah NAEFS Downscale:	Skyway Point, CO
Main Orientation:	North
Average Annual Snowfall:	250"
ZRankings Average Annual Snowfall:	225"

Sitting on the north side of the Grand Mesa, Powderhorn's name is well-founded as it is just above the high desert on the western slope. This gives it tremendously light powder.

Name:	**Purgatory**
Website:	Purgatoryresort.com
Nearest City:	Durango
Ski Area Information:	
Acreage:	1,605 acres
Snowmaking acreage:	320 acres
Top Elevation:	10,822'

Vertical Drop:	2,029'
Typical Ski Season:	Late November to Late April
Favored Wind Directions for Snowfall:	Southwest (also west)
Nearby Univ. Utah NAEFS Downscale:	Coal Bank Pass, CO
Main Orientation:	North
Average Annual Snowfall:	260"
ZRankings Average Annual Snowfall:	264"
Nearby Cat Skiing Operations:	At the resort (Purgatory Snowcat Adventures)

Purgatory is the largest ski resort near Durango. It can get pummeled from storms coming from the Southwest, leading to a paradise for powder skiers – lots of terrain and lots of snow.

Name:	**Silverton Mountain**
Website:	silvertonmountain.com
Nearest City:	Silverton
Ski Area Information:	
Acreage:	26,819 acres[60]
Snowmaking Acreage:	None
Top Elevation:	13,487'
Vertical Drop:	3,887'
Typical Ski Season:	late-December to late-April
Favored Wind Directions for Snowfall:	West (also northwest, southwest, and north)
Nearby Univ. Utah NAEFS Downscale:	Red Mt Pass, CO
Main Orientation:	Northwest

---

[60]   This number is based upon total acreage including helicopter drops.

Average Annual Snowfall:	400"
Nearby Heli Skiing Operations:	At the resort.
Popular Backcountry with Similar Snow:	Red Mountain Pass

Silverton is the only resort of its kind in the country, if not the world. No snowmaking. No grooming. No crowds. An avalanche beacon, shovel, and probe are required to ride the lift. And, there's only one lift. The one double chairlift, coupled with a little hiking, accesses thousands and thousands of acres of terrain. Silverton is properly known as one of the great expert mountains in the world.

Name:	**Ski Cooper**
Website:	skicooper.com
Nearest City:	Leadville
Ski Area Information:	
Acreage:	470 acres
Snowmaking acreage:	None
Top Elevation:	11,700'
Vertical Drop:	1,200'
Typical Ski Season:	Early December to mid-April
Favored Wind Directions for Snowfall:	West (also southwest, northwest)
Nearby Univ. Utah NAEFS Downscale:	n/a
Main Orientation:	Northwest
Average Annual Snowfall:	260"
Nearby Cat Skiing Operations:	At the resort (Chicago Ridge)
Popular Backcountry with Similar Snow:	Tennessee Pass

The Tenth Mountain Division trained by Ski Cooper in preparation for winter warfare in World War 2, and Ski Cooper remains today as a beloved local mountain. It does not have a single snowmaking machine to interfere with the pristine snow that falls on the mountain.

Name:	**Snowmass**
Website:	aspensnowmass.com
Nearest City:	Snowmass Village
Ski Area Information:	
Acreage:	3,332 acres
Snowmaking Acreage:	256 acres
Top Elevation:	12,510'
Vertical Drop:	4,406'
Typical Ski Season:	Late November to mid-April
Favored Wind Directions for Snowfall:	West (also northwest and southwest)
Nearby Univ. Utah NAEFS Downscale:	Aspen Airport, CO and McClure Pass, CO
Main Orientation:	North
Average Annual Snowfall:	300"
ZRankings Average Annual Snowfall:	295"
Nearby Cat Skiing Operations:	At Aspen Mountain and Aspen Highlands
Popular Backcountry with Similar Snow:	Alfred Braun Hut System

If Colorado's biggest ski area is defined by vertical drop, Snowmass is Colorado's biggest ski area. And it isn't just the tallest ski area by statistics, the mountain feels huge. Unsurprisingly, it has an extraordinary amount of places to seek out great powder.

Name:	**Steamboat**
Website:	steamboat.com

Nearest City:	Steamboat Springs
Ski Area Information:	
Acreage:	2,965 acres
Snowmaking acreage:	375 acres
Top Elevation:	10,568'
Vertical Drop:	3,668'
Typical Ski Season:	late-November to mid-April
Favored Wind Directions for Snowfall:	West (also southwest and northwest)
Nearby Univ. Utah NAEFS Downscale:	Steamboat-SPL, CO
Main Orientation:	West
Average Annual Snowfall:	375"
ZRankings Average Annual Snowfall:	368"
Nearby Cat Skiing Operations:	Steamboat Powdercats
Popular Backcountry with Similar Snow:	Buffalo Pass

Steamboat is world famous for its Champagne Powder® snow[61] – named by a local because the powder would tickle the bottom of his nose just like Champagne. There may not be any other spot in the world that gets as much ultra-low density powder as Steamboat.

Name:	**Sunlight**
Website:	sunlightmtn.com
Nearest City:	Glenwood Springs
Ski Area Information:	
Acreage:	680 acres

---

[61] Registered Trademark of Steamboat Ski & Resort Corporation, used by permission.

Snowmaking acreage:	21 acres
Top Elevation:	9,895'
Vertical Drop:	2,015'
Typical Ski Season:	mid-December to early-April
Favored Wind Directions for Snowfall:	West (also southwest and northwest)
Nearby Univ. Utah NAEFS Downscale:	McClure Pass, CO
Main Orientation:	North
Average Annual Snowfall:	250"
ZRankings Average Annual Snowfall:	232"

Imagine a ski area between Snowmass and Vail, with as many acres of skiable terrain as Aspen Mountain. Add to that mix only a small handful of fixed grip chairlifts in total, which means fewer skiers to ski out the countless powder stashes. That is Sunlight. Need I say more?

Name:	**Telluride**
Website:	tellurideskiresort.com
Nearest City:	Telluride
Ski Area Information:	
Acreage:	2,000 acres
Snowmaking Acreage:	220 acres
Top Elevation:	13,150'
Vertical Drop:	4,400'
Typical Ski Season:	late-November to early-April
Favored Wind Directions for Snowfall:	West (also northwest, southwest, and north)
Nearby Univ. Utah NAEFS Downscale:	Telluride Airport
Main Orientation:	North
Average Annual Snowfall:	280"

ZRankings Average Annual Snowfall:	276"
Nearby Heli Skiing Operations:	Helitrax
Popular Backcountry with Similar Snow:	Red Mountain Pass

Telluride is the most famous ski resort in the San Juan mountain range, and justifiably so. From a steep face filled with bumps right above town to amazing high alpine bowl skiing to its two great ski towns connected by a gondola – Telluride has it all.

Name:	**Vail**
Website:	vail.com
Nearest City:	Vail
Ski Area Information:	
Acreage:	5,317 acres
Snowmaking acreage:	461 acres
Top Elevation:	11,570'
Vertical Drop:	3,450'
Typical Ski Season:	mid-November to mid-April
Favored Wind Directions for Snowfall:	West (also southwest, northwest)
Nearby Univ. Utah NAEFS Downscale:	Vail Pass, CO
Main Orientation:	North
Average Annual Snowfall:	354"
ZRankings Average Annual Snowfall:	354"
Nearby Cat Skiing Operations:	Vail Powder Guides
Popular Backcountry with Similar Snow:	Vail Pass

If Colorado's biggest ski area is defined by lift accessible skiable acreage, Vail is easily Colorado's biggest ski area. Vail's vast back bowls are known throughout the world. And, with over 5000 acres of terrain, there are endless places to find powder at Vail.

Name:	**Winter Park**
Website:	winterparkresort.com
Nearest City:	Winter Park
Ski Area Information:	
Acreage:	3,081 acres
Snowmaking acreage:	313 acres
Top Elevation:	12,060'
Vertical Drop:	3,060'
Typical Ski Season:	Late November to Early May
Favored Wind Directions for Snowfall:	Northwest (also west, north, southeast, and east)
Nearby Univ. Utah NAEFS Downscale:	Berthoud Pass, CO
Main Orientation:	Northeast
Average Annual Snowfall:	348"
ZRankings Average Annual Snowfall:	347"
Nearby Cat Skiing Operations:	Powder Addiction and at the resort
Popular Backcountry with Similar Snow:	Berthoud Pass

Winter Park has everything that powder skiers look for – trees, steeps, cliffs, high alpine terrain, and lots of skiable acres. It gets hammered with northwest storms, and even picks up some snow from upslope storms. And, Winter Park is the only major ski area near Denver that avoids many of the worst traffic sections of I-70.

Name:	**Wolf Creek**
Website:	wolfcreekski.com
Nearest City:	South Fork

Ski Area Information:

Acreage:	1600 acres
Snowmaking acreage:	5 acres
Top Elevation:	11,904'
Vertical Drop:	1,904'
Typical Ski Season:	early November to early April
Favored Wind Directions for Snowfall:	Southwest (also west, east, southeast)
Nearby Univ. Utah NAEFS Downscale:	Wolf Creek Pass, CO
Main Orientation:	Northeast
Average Annual Snowfall:	430"
ZRankings Average Annual Snowfall:	387"
Nearby Cat Skiing Operations:	At the resort
Popular Backcountry with Similar Snow:	Wolf Creek Pass

Wolf Creek gets the most snow of any ski area in Colorado. Period. That may be the highest praise any ski area can ever receive.

Appendix B

Snowfall Percentages by Month of the Year at Select Locations

Below are the percent of yearly snowfall by month for multiple popular ski area and backcountry locations throughout Colorado. I chose these locations to be representative of the different Colorado climatic locations. Please note that when the location is a town (e.g., Vail), the data is from the town, so it tends to slightly overestimate snow during the coldest months (e.g., January) and underestimate it in warmer months where it's snowing at the summit but not at the base (e.g., April).

This data is from the Western Regional Climate Center's long-term analyses. Instead of providing the information in inches per month, the appendix provides it as percentage of total. I thought it would be misleading to provide snowfall in inches as that would be comparing apples (mountain measurement sites) with oranges (town measurement sites).[62] So, percentage gives a better overall sense of which months have more or less snow. All percentages are the average percentage of the yearly total.

---

[62] Frankly, I've never understood the phrase of comparing apples to oranges, as apples are way better than oranges. Especially honey crisp apples.

Aspen (Classic Colorado):

October Snowfall:	6%
November Snowfall:	14%
December Snowfall:	16%
January Snowfall:	16%
February Snowfall:	16%
March Snowfall:	16%
April Snowfall:	10%
May Snowfall:	3%

Berthoud Pass (Continental Divide):

September Snowfall:	2%
October Snowfall:	7%
November Snowfall:	13%
December Snowfall:	13%
January Snowfall:	13%
February Snowfall:	11%
March Snowfall:	15%
April Snowfall:	14%
May Snowfall:	9%
June Snowfall:	3%

Breckenridge (Continental Divide):

September Snowfall:	2%
October Snowfall:	7%
November Snowfall:	14%
December Snowfall:	14%
January Snowfall:	13%

February Snowfall: 13%
March Snowfall: 15%
April Snowfall: 14%
May Snowfall: 6%

Coal Creek Canyon (somewhat near Eldora – East of the Continental Divide):

September Snowfall: 2%
October Snowfall: 9%
November Snowfall: 8%
December Snowfall: 12%
January Snowfall: 9%
February Snowfall: 9%
March Snowfall: 19%
April Snowfall: 24%
May Snowfall: 8%

Echo Mountain (technically Squaw Mountain – East of the Continental Divide):

September Snowfall: 5%
October Snowfall: 8%
November Snowfall: 10%
December Snowfall: 8%
January Snowfall: 5%
February Snowfall: 9%
March Snowfall: 17%
April Snowfall: 19%
May Snowfall: 14%
June Snowfall: 4%

Powderhorn (Classic Colorado):

October Snowfall:	6%
November Snowfall:	12%
December Snowfall:	15%
January Snowfall:	18%
February Snowfall:	13%
March Snowfall:	16%
April Snowfall:	14%
May Snowfall:	5%

Telluride (Classic Colorado):

October Snowfall:	5%
November Snowfall:	13%
December Snowfall:	15%
January Snowfall:	15%
February Snowfall:	14%
March Snowfall:	18%
April Snowfall:	12%
May Snowfall:	4%

Vail (Classic Colorado):

October Snowfall:	4%
November Snowfall:	15%
December Snowfall:	15%
January Snowfall:	19%
February Snowfall:	18%
March Snowfall	13%
April Snowfall:	12%
May Snowfall:	3%

Winter Park (Continental Divide):

September Snowfall:	1%
October Snowfall:	5%
November Snowfall:	13%
December Snowfall:	16%
January Snowfall:	16%
February Snowfall:	14%
March Snowfall:	16%
April Snowfall:	14%
May Snowfall:	5%

Wolf Creek (technically one mile east of Wolf Creek – Wolf Creek Pass):

October Snowfall:	6%
November Snowfall:	13%
December Snowfall:	18%
January Snowfall:	17%
February Snowfall:	15%
March Snowfall:	18%
April Snowfall:	10%
May Snowfall:	3%

Appendix C

Climate Change and St. Mary's Glacier

Unfortunately, the earth's average temperature has been rising over the last hundred years. Everywhere one reads about receding glaciers as a result of this climate change. Is Colorado seeing the same effects? Are our cirque glaciers slowly disappearing? How will skiing change?

The following analysis is simply based upon my own observations. As briefly discussed in Chapter 18, there are numerous problems with relying simply upon human observation. That said, based upon my observations, there is both good news and bad news.

The bad news is over the last two dozen years since I've been skiing Colorado's cirque glaciers, our cirque glaciers are certainly shrinking. And, this is consistent with more long-term analysis by others.

The good news is that our cirque glaciers do not appear to be receding / shrinking nearly as fast as many glaciers elsewhere. From personal observations, the glaciers are receding / shrinking at a terrifying rate in places such as the Canadian Rockies, the Alps, and Glacier National Park. While our cirque glaciers are shrinking, if our comparatively tiny glaciers were in any of these locations, they would have mostly disappeared by now. Put another way, any snowfield / glacier the size of just St. Mary's Glacier would have disappeared already in Montana, Alberta, or the Alps. So, while Colorado is feeling the effects of climate change, hopefully it'll be at a slower rate than much of the rest of the world.

Here is some background and analysis on the shrinking of St. Mary's Glacier. St. Mary's Glacier is at its smallest size each year between mid-September and mid-October. I skied St. Mary's Glacier on-and-off during the September and October time frame from 1996 through 2003. And, I have skied St. Mary's Glacier consistently during the September and October time frame every year since 2004. Being the skiing nerd that I am, I keep a ski diary with notes on every day I've skied.

St. Mary's Glacier always had a typical shape late in the season from 1996 through 2006. (That said, I missed skiing it during the summer of 2002, which was a particularly bad snow year, and in which it probably broke into separate sections). In 2007 for the first time that I ever witnessed, the upper third of the glacier disconnected with the lower two thirds, and then the lower two-thirds split into two pieces. Since that time, similar disconnections and shrinkage occurred, with a couple of years the top third melting out completely after it disconnected from the lower two-thirds of the glacier.

If it helps, here are my observations from September 1 to October 31 each year that I've had records from 1996 to present. Normal means the glacier retained its usual shape. Small means it broke into two pieces. Very small means it broke into three pieces. Extremely small means not only did it break into three pieces, but also that the top third melted out. The footnotes record the observation dates, the glacier status, and when new snow started to fall. When new snow started to fall, on all days listed, it was still obvious where the old / permanent snow began and ended.

1996 – Normal[63]
1997 – Normal[64]
1999 – Normal[65]
2004 – Normal[66]

---

[63] Normal on 10/20/96 (new snow already starting to accumulate).

[64] Normal on 9/20/97, 10/5/97.

[65] Normal on 10/23/99 (new snow already starting to accumulate).

[66] Normal on 9/5/04, 9/22/04 (new snow already starting to accumulate), 9/26/04 (same), 10/3/04 (same), 10/16/04 (same).

2005 – Normal[67]
2006 – Normal[68]
2007 –Very Small[69]
2008 – Normal[70]
2009 – Small[71]
2010 –Very Small[72]
2011 – Normal[73]
2012 – Extremely Small[74]
2013 –Very Small[75]
2014 –Very Small[76]
2015 –Very Small[77]
2016 – Small[78]
2017 –Very Small[79]

---

[67] Normal on 9/10/05, 9/24/05, 10/15/05 (new snow already starting to accumulate).

[68] Normal on 9/9/06.

[69] Normal on 9/1/07, small on 9/16/07, 9/19/07, 9/25/07, 10/4/07, and very small on 10/7/07.

[70] Normal on 9/2/08, 10/12/08 (new snow starting to accumulate).

[71] Small on 9/26/09 (new snow starting to accumulate), 10/11/09 (same).

[72] Small on 9/5/10, Very Small 10/10/10 (new snow starting to accumulate).

[73] Normal on 9/21/11, 10/1/11, 10/9/11 (new snow starting to accumulate).

[74] Very small on 9/9/12, extremely small on 10/7/12, 10/14/12 (new snow starting to accumulate).

[75] Very small on 9/1/13, 9/21/13, 9/24/13 (new snow starting to accumulate), 10/13/13 (same).

[76] Very small on 9/28/14, 10/11/14 (new snow starting to accumulate).

[77] Very small on 9/24/15, 10/11/15.

[78] Normal on 9/5/16; small on 10/9/16. Note, without good early season snowfalls, I went to St. Mary's on 11/11/16, and glacier was very small.

[79] Normal on 9/4/17; very small on 9/29/17, 10/13/17 (new snow starting to accumulate).

2018 – Extremely Small[80]
2019 – Very Small[81]
2020 – Small[82]

Sadly, in the not-too-distant future, St. Mary's Glacier will be no more. It's still hanging in there, but another year like 2012, without early season snowfall to stop the melt, might mean that St. Mary's Glacier will no longer be a permanent snowfield. Hopefully, our larger glaciers like Andrews Glacier will stick around for a while. It's tragic, however, that at some point soon St. Mary's Glacier will be a thing of the past. I take my children to ski St. Mary's Glacier all summer long, and I'm heartbroken that my children likely will not be able to take their children to ski St. Mary's Glacier all summer long.

---

[80] Very small on 9/2/18, extremely small on 10/3/18.
[81] Normal on 9/10/19; normal on 9/24/19; very small on 10/12/19 (new snow starting to accumulate).
[82] Normal on 9/1/20; small on 9/10/20; small on 10/1/20.

Appendix D

Dates of the First Ski Area to Open in Colorado

Colorado ski areas race each other with snowmaking (and occasionally natural snow) to be the first resort to open in the state, and often the nation. The race to be first open is not without its comical pettiness. Back in the 1990s Keystone and Loveland competed every year to be the first open. One year, if memory serves me right (not that it always does) when both ski areas were opening on the same day, after Keystone announced a 9 am opening, Loveland announced that they'd open at 8 am to be the first ski area open. The next year, Keystone (which has lights for night skiing) outdid Loveland by turning on its lights at 6 am to beat Loveland as the first ski area to open by several hours.

Starting in the early 2000s, A–Basin installed snowmaking and joined the race. Keystone dropped out of the race for a little over a decade, but then in 2019 Keystone rejoined the race to make it a three-way contest. The comical one-upmanship of the 1990s had nothing on 2019. On the morning of October 11, 2019, Keystone announced that it would be the first ski area in the state (and nation) to open the next day, on October 12. Then, around 2 pm that afternoon of October 11, A–Basin announced it would open at 3:30 pm that afternoon for two hours of skiing, to beat Keystone as the first ski area open. It will be entertaining to watch the shenanigans between the resorts in future years as they compete to open.

Below is a list of the first day a Colorado ski area opened for the ski season, and which ski area won the title as the first ski area open. The list goes back a couple of decades to the year when I first moved to Colorado. For those who are overly curious, the earliest opening date was October 7, 2009 and the latest day was October 29, 2015. The multi-decade average (mean) as well as median opening day is basically October 17.

Please note that although as a total ski geek I keep fairly good records of opening day each year, I did not write down the day every single year. So, for some of the below years I had to rely upon various internet sources. So, while generally accurate, there may be a couple of mistakes in this list. Apologies to the various ski resorts to the extent there are errors.

2020:	Wolf Creek on October 28
2019:	A-Basin on October 11
2018:	Wolf Creek on October 13
2017:	A-Basin on October 13
2016:	A-Basin on October 21
2015:	Loveland on October 29
2014:	A-Basin on October 17
2013:	A-Basin on October 13
2012:	A-Basin on October 17
2011:	Wolf Creek on October 8
2010:	Loveland on October 24
2009:	Loveland on October 7
2008:	A-Basin and Loveland (tie) on October 15
2007:	A-Basin on October 10
2006:	A-Basin on October 13
2005:	Loveland on October 14
2004:	Loveland on October 15
2003:	Loveland on October 28
2002:	Loveland on October 17
2001:	Copper on October 17
2000:	Loveland on October 20
1999:	Loveland on October 19
1998:	Loveland on October 13
1997:	Keystone and Loveland (tie) on October 17
1996:	Keystone and Loveland (tie) on October 21

Appendix E

Useful Websites

To the extent it helps, below are the weather websites I have as favorites on my phone and on my desktop. These are purely my own preferences, and I'm literally providing them below based solely on what's in my favorites collection in both my phone and on my desktop. When there's no good direct link, I simply note the main webpage and that it provides "access to" my favorite information. As a few of the websites don't work well on my iPhone, I list them separately.

This list, to keep it from being too biased towards my neck of the woods, will only include the weather prediction websites. I won't bore you with my favorite webcams and Snotel websites as they're mostly for the ski areas and backcountry areas near my house.

FORECAST DISCUSSIONS

https://forecast.weather.gov/ – National Weather Service's webpage that provides access to the National Weather Service Area Forecast Discussion (Denver/Boulder) and National Weather Service Area Forecast Discussion (Grand Junction)

https://avalanche.state.co.us/forecasts/weather/zone-forecast/–Colorado Avalanche Information Center's Zone Weather Forecast

https://opensnow.com/dailysnow/colorado – Open Snow's Colorado Daily Snow

https://powderchasers.com/ – Powderchasers (Home Page)

http://www.indianpeaksweather.net/ – Indian Peaks Weather

https://bmnsp.org/weather-forecast/ – Bryan Mountain Nordic Ski Patrol's Weather Forecast (on my phone for self-punishment, so I can see all my goofs on my weather predictions and my endless typos)

MODEL ACCESS AND OTHER TOOLS

https://avalanche.state.co.us/forecasts/weather/point-forecasts/–Colorado Avalanche Information Center's WRF Point Forecasts

https://spotwx.com/ – SpotWx – Providing American Model and Canadian Model Point Forecasts

http://weather.utah.edu/ – University of Utah's Weather Center webpage, that provides access to the NAEFS-Downscaled Plumes

http://wxmaps.org/fcst.php – George Mason University's Model Analysis and Forecast Maps

https://www.weather.gov/oun/sfcmaps – National Weather Service's Current Surface Map

https://www.weather.gov/oun/upperairdata – National Weather Service's Current Upper Air Maps

MODEL ACCESS (DESKTOP FRIENDLY ONLY)

https://mag.ncep.noaa.gov/model-guidance-model-area.php–American Models and Ensemble Models

https://weather.gc.ca/model_forecast/model_e.html – Canadian Models

https://avalanche.state.co.us/forecasts/weather/model-forecasts/ – Colorado Avalanche Information Center's WRF Model

https://www.pivotalweather.com/model.php – Various American, Canadian, and European Models

Appendix F

Further Reading and Further Education

Has this book just whet your appetite to learn more? Below is a collection of books by topic, and I should note that the book by Jim Steenburgh (a/k/a Professor Powder) is definitely a must read. If you want to learn more in a classroom setting, the CAIC offers a Mountain Meteorology 3-Day Intensive Workshop, which is fantastic. And, if you simply want to learn a lot more about weather in lecture format on your smart phone, the Great Courses app has an outstanding course by Robert Fovell in meteorology.

WEATHER (NON-TECHNICAL) BOOKS

- Andrew Blum, *The Weather Machine: A Journey Inside the Forecast* (2019).
- William Burroughs, *Mountain Weather: A Guide for Skiers and Hillwalkers* (1995).
- Storm Dunlap, *Guide to Weather Forecasting: All the Information You'll Need to Make Your Own Weather Forecast* (2010).
- Christopher Dewdney, *18 Miles, The Epic Drama of Our Atmosphere and Weather* (2018).
- Kenneth Libbrecht & Rachel Wing, *The Snowflake: Winter's Frozen Artistry* (2015).
- Mike Nelson, *Colorado Weather Almanac* (2007).

- Tish Rabe, *Oh Say Can You Say What's the Weather Today? All About Weather* (2004).
- Jeff Renner, *Mountain Weather: Backcountry Forecasting for Hikers, Campers, Climbers, Skiers, Snowboarders* (2005).
- Jim Steenburgh, *Secrets of the Greatest Snow on Earth: Weather, Climate Change, and Finding Deep Powder in Utah's Wasatch Mountains and around the World* (2014).
- Jack Williams, *The Weather Book: An Easy-to-Understand Guide to the USA's Weather* (1997).
- Paul Yeager, *Weather Whys: Facts, Myths, and Oddities* (2010).

WEATHER (TECHNICAL) BOOKS

- C. Donald Ahrens, *Essentials of Meteorology: An Invitation to the Atmosphere* (2017).
- Roger G. Barry, *Mountain Weather and Climate* (2008).
- Nolan J. Doesken & Arthur Judson, *The Snow Booklet, A Guide to the Science, Climatology, and Measurement of Snow in the United States* (1997).
- C. David Whiteman, *Mountain Meteorology: Fundamentals and Applications* (2000).

AVALANCHE (NON-TECHNICAL) BOOKS

- Tony Daffern, *Backcountry Avalanche Safety: A Guide to Managing Avalanche Risk* (2018).
- Jill Fredston & Doug Fesler, *Snow Sense: A Guide to Evaluating Snow Avalanche Hazards* (2011).
- Sue Ferguson & Ed LaChapelle, *The ABCs of Avalanche Safety* (2003).
- Bruce Tremper, *Staying Alive in Avalanche Terrain* (2018).

AVALANCHE (TECHNICAL) BOOKS

- David McClung and Peter Schaerer, *The Avalanche Handbook* (2006).

MEDICAL BOOKS

- Edward C. McNamara, et al., *Outdoor Emergency Care* (2020).

COLORADO BACKCOUNTRY SKIING GUIDEBOOKS

- Lou Dawson, *Dawson's Guide to Colorado Backcountry Skiing, Volume 1* (2000).
- Ron Haddad & Eileen Faughery, *Indian Peak Descents: Ski Mountaineering & Snowboarding in Colorado's Indian Peaks* (1996).
- Ron Haddad & Eileen Faughery, *Front Range Descents: Spring & Summer Skiing & Snowboarding in Colorado's Front Range* (2003).
- Mark Kelly, *Backcountry Skiing and Ski Mountaineering in Rocky Mountain National Park* (2013).
- Brittany Konsella and Frank Konsella, *Backcountry Ski & Snowboard Routes: Colorado* (2017).
- Jordan Lipp, *Backcountry Skiing Berthoud Pass: A Guidebook to Backcountry Skiing and Snowboarding Berthoud Pass, Colorado* (2005).[83]
- Brian Litz, *Colorado Hut to Hut: Guide to Skiing, Hiking and Biking Colorado's Backcountry Cabins* (2000).
- Brian Litz & Kurt Lankford, *Skiing Colorado's Backcountry: Northern Mountains – Trails & Tours* (1989).
- Fritz Sperry, *Making Turns in Colorado's Front Range* (2016).
- Fritz Sperry, *Making Turns in the Tenmile-Mosquito Range* (2012).

SKI AREA OPERATIONS AND BUSINESS BOOKS

- Chris Diamond, *Ski Inc. 2020* (2019).

---

[83] If one was to list the three greatest and most influential books written in the last 200 years, the three books would probably be Charles Darwin's *On the Origins of Species*, Stephen Hawking's *A Brief History of Time*, and Jordan Lipp's *Backcountry Skiing Berthoud Pass*.

- Mathieu Fauve, Hansueli Rhyner, & Martin Schneebeli, *Preparation and Maintenance of Pistes: Handbook for Practitioners* (2002).
- Patrick Torsell, *Snow Guns Before Sunrise: A Peek Behind the Veil of Ski Resort Operations* (2017).

Appendix G

Which Model is the Best Model?

Some folks may wonder, which model is the best model? This is the one and only question in this book where my actual day job comes to the forefront. In case you somehow haven't already figured it out, I am not a meteorologist, climatologist, or some other sort of atmospheric scientist. And, I would hope that my lack of specialized training makes you more optimistic about your ability to be a great powder hunter. You don't need a specific degree to be good at hunting powder, as hopefully this book demonstrates. Rather, with a little book learning and some practical experience, anyone with an internet connection can learn the ropes of forecasting well enough to be a successful powder hunter.

My day job is as an attorney. And for the first and only time in this book, I think it's worth referencing the law. In Court, if a witness asked the question, "which [weather] model is the best model," I would likely stand up and object to the question. It's a horrible question. It first assumes a fact not in evidence – that there is a best model. The very premise of the question is wrong – as each model has its good days and its bad days.

The next problem with the question "which model is the best model" is that it assumes that one model is better at everything than every other model. But, are you looking at the ability of a model to predict the path of a hurricane in the Atlantic Ocean, the wind speed atop Mount Washington, or the amount of snowfall in the Atlas Mountains of Morocco?

The third problem with the question is that it ignores time. The models are constantly evolving. As more information becomes available and computer processing speeds increase, the models continually improve. When the models are constantly improving, it's hard to compare various models.

So, I don't think one can fairly begin to answer the question of which model is the best. To the extent it's helpful, I can (sort of) answer the question of which model does the best job, as long as we limit the question to (1) predicting snow (the most important thing), (2) in my backcountry ski patrol zone (East of the Continental Divide), and (3) during the 2019-2020 ski season.

So, with these limitations, the best model is … drum roll please …. The CAIC WRF Hi-Res model.

If you're interested in how the sausage was made for me to reach this conclusion, read on. If you're not interested, which I completely understand, feel free to skip to the next appendix section.

Okay, now that you've been more than warned to skip to the next chapter unless you want to go down the rabbit hole of my analysis, here we go. During the 2019-2020 ski season, in my weather forecasts for my backcountry ski patrol, I tried to get more than an anecdotal sense of how each of the major numerical weather models performed throughout the season. So, in every forecast where I could, I had a retrospective discussion where I compared the snowfall that occurred to what each model predicted. In those discussions, I noted each model when it performed particularly well or particularly poorly as to snowfall predictions.

At the end of the season, I put pencil to paper to figure out how the models performed, comparing total references to models with the number of compliments or insults I doled out in my retrospective discussions.

This analysis is, admittedly, rather subjective. It's based upon my own take in calling models out in my retrospective discussions. Perhaps to put it more bluntly, this isn't true science. Rather its running numbers based upon my somewhat subjective and varying comments on how well or poorly models did. Also, it's worth noting that for the first month of forecasts I wasn't doing as good of a job comparing how the models predicted snow versus what occurred. And, in mid-March I lost the ability to judge results on the Eldora Snow stake Webcam due to COVID-19 shutting down Eldora – so I had to compare the forecasts with the less reliable Snotel data of how much snow actually fell. Nevertheless, I still think this analysis is quite interesting and enlightening.

In analyzing the models, I thought it was only fair to limit the analysis to the models I referred to by name in more than ten forecasts, as there just wasn't sufficient data on the other models. I referenced by name the American and Canadian models 44 times, the European Model 31 times, the WRF model 30 times, and the NAM model 21 times. All other models (e.g., HRRR, RDPS) I referenced fewer than 10 times.

Good calls overall – First, I compared the total number of references in the forecasts to the number of times I remarked in the recap discussion how accurate any particular model turned out to be in snowfall prediction. Here are the percentages of times I complimented a model for doing a nice job. NAM – 29%; WRF – 27%; Canadian – 23%; European – 23%; American – 18%. It's not surprising that the regional shorter-term models (i.e., the NAM and WRF) outperformed the global medium-term models – as among other things I didn't break out the numbers by how far away the forecasts were. The one surprise from all of this is how poorly the American model performed. But wait, things are about to get both more interesting and more confusing.

Bad calls overall – Second, I compared the number of times I criticized each of the models in a recap to the total references in forecasts. The numbers were interesting, and to some extent an unexpected flip of the good call numbers. I criticized the models the following percent of forecasts: NAM – 43%; Canadian – 36%; European – 35%; WRF – 33%; American – 27%. So, just looking at good calls overall and bad calls overall – it's hard to reach meaningful conclusions except the WRF seems to be above average in good calls and below average in bad calls.

Too optimistic – I next looked at how often the models overpredicted snowfall. Overall, I called out the Canadian Model the most number of times for being too optimistic, but it was never ridiculously over optimistic. Only four times the whole season did I call out a model for being utterly embarrassing in how overly optimistic it was in its snow forecast, twice with the American and twice with the WRF. So, when the Canadian, European, or NAM models were predicting gigantic snowfalls, not once were there not at least somewhat significant snowfalls. Weighted numbers of how often a model was too optimistic are as follows (labeled as a percent, though not technically a percent): WRF – 23%; Canadian – 14%; American – 11%; European – 10%; NAM – 5%. In other words, the most likely to overpredict snow is the WRF, and least likely to overpredict snow is the NAM.

Too pessimistic – With the lone exception of the WRF Model, the models all tended to underpredict snow a lot more often than they overpredicted snow, which is a bit surprising. In fact, only the WRF Model had the same amount of overpredictions as underpredictions. I've often faulted (based upon my own anecdotal experience) the University of Utah's downscaled ensemble (based upon the American and Canadian ensemble models) for being too optimistic – and I generally worry that the regular models are too optimistic. So, I wasn't expecting when I put pen to paper that all the models except for the WRF Model in my patrol zone were too pessimistic. Weighted numbers of how often a model was too pessimistic is as follows (labeled as a percent, though not technically a percent): NAM – 57%; European – 42%; American – 36%; Canadian – 31%; WRF – 23%.

So, what are the lessons learned as to each of the models?

If I had to pick the best model of the season, it was the WRF model. All the other models tended overall to underpredict snow, while the WRF seemed even in its over and underprediction. And, it was the only model to be above average in total good calls and below average on total bad calls.

Although there was no clear runner-up, if I had to pick the Silver Medal, I'd say overall it was the Canadian (GDPS) Model.

Quite surprisingly, my analysis didn't favor the regional models over the global models. While the WRF did the best, I would have thought that the NAM Model would have either gotten the gold or silver in predictions as it's a regional model. However, the NAM Model had a rather poor showing. The NAM Model was the worst offender for underpredicting, though in fairness to it, it received the most compliments for good forecasting through the year.

Also interesting was that the conventional wisdom, backed up by multiple studies, on the most accurate models generally seems to have no correlation to the little corner of the world I was forecasting. The European Model is generally considered to be the best global model in the world, with the American Model second, and the Canadian Model third. However, when looking at snowfall in my backcountry patrol zone, neither the European nor American models did particularly well, and probably the Canadian model was just slightly more accurate overall.

In sum, it was an ugly and confusing fight between the models, but the WRF Model came out on top.

Appendix H

Why I Wrote This Book

I suppose it is rather narcissistic to write about why I wrote this book. At least I've relegated this discussion, as self-centered as it is, to an appendix topic as opposed to an actual chapter of the book.

The first book I ever wrote was a backcountry skiing guidebook to the Berthoud Pass region, titled: *Backcountry Skiing Berthoud Pass: A Guidebook to Skiing and Snowboarding Berthoud Pass, Colorado*. I wrote that book for a very different reason than any other book. As a ski patroller at Berthoud Pass during the late 1990s, once the ski area shut down, I was worried about the loss of knowledge as time passed and memories faded. I had already seen this happen talking with friends who had ski patrolled at the old Geneva Basin and Hidden Valley ski areas, which shut down long before Berthoud Pass ski area had shut down. I would ask these former Geneva Basin and Hidden Valley patrollers detailed questions about avalanche patterns, wind patterns, and their avalanche mitigation work, so I'd have a better idea of where to backcountry ski at these once great ski areas. Inevitably, the former patrollers had forgotten the critical details. I did not want the same knowledge loss to happen with Berthoud Pass. Most of the guidebook was a collection and recording of the collective knowledge, names, and information about this amazing place to aid future backcountry skiers. This was information I did not want lost to time. I still refer to my own guidebook when I forget route names, or I want a reminder of what was the patrol consensus (from two decades ago now) on slide danger and sweet spots of particular lines. I'm glad to have done my piece in preserving knowledge.

The next book I wrote was for a very different purpose — with my day job as a high-stakes product liability defense attorney, I always wanted a book that was a one-stop-shop for an overview of all the legal issues on which I worked. It didn't exist. So, I wrote the book I originally wished someone else would have written — *Product Liability Law & Procedure in Colorado*. As an aside, being a legal author is quite lucrative — my royalties from this book will twice a year pay for me to take my kids to Noodles & Company. If my wife wants to join us at Noodles, the bi-annual royalties usually at that point aren't enough to pay for all four of us.

My other passion besides skiing, is wine. And like the product liability book, I wrote my third book (with my wife) — *Is There Apple Juice in My Wine?: Thirty-Eight Laws that Affect the Wine You Drink* — simply because it was a topic I really wanted to read a book about and no one else had written the book.

Which brings me to this book. As soon as I read in Joel Gratz' Open Snow blog about Jim Steenburgh's book *Secrets of the Greatest Snow on Earth: Weather, Climate Change, and Finding Deep Powder in Utah's Wasatch Mountains and around the World*, I purchased the book. I devoured *Secrets of the Greatest Snow on Earth* cover to cover. That was in late 2014, and I instantly wished someone would write a book about hunting powder in my backyard, Colorado. As no one had, in June of 2015 I started working on this book (long before I even conceived the idea of my wine book).

But I am not an atmospheric scientist, and I have no degree in meteorology. My day job is about as far away from the science of weather as one can get. But I do love to write. And, as I was already pretty proficient at hunting powder based upon weather models and my knowledge of local topography, I thought that if no one else was going to write this book, I might as well do my best. I read (and often reread) every book listed in Appendix F. I took the CAIC's mountain meteorology class. To make sure my general scientific knowledge wasn't too horribly bad, I went through the Great Courses lectures on meteorology (three times), thermodynamics, chaos theory, as well as individual lectures on fluid mechanics (as Great Courses does not have a full course on fluid mechanics). And, I started weather forecasting for my back-country ski patrol. After all, it's one thing to create personal forecasts for the sake of your own powder searches – it's a different thing to put into writing your weather predictions for your fellow ski patrollers to read (and be mercilessly mocked when you're wrong). I stole as many of my own (hopefully) entertaining avalanche safety class lecture points and translated them into the written page. And, I figured if journalists and writers can and have written great books on the weather, why can't I give it a shot?

In the end, I've learned so much writing this book, I'm oddly grateful that a book on hunting Colorado powder did not already exist. As this book had not already been written by someone else, the writing of it forced me to learn far more than I ever could have learned from simply reading it. That said, as I'm not an atmospheric scientist, I can only hope that this book inspires someone to become an atmospheric scientist and engage in the rigorous study of Colorado's powder. While there are certainly studies on Colorado snow patterns, there are fewer than one would have expected. Someday, armed with future advances in knowledge, I cannot wait for that person (hopefully inspired by this book) to write a far better book than this one. I can't wait to buy that book and read it.

Glossary of Terms, and Whether They're Good or Bad

Unfortunately, I've had to use some big words in this book. If it helps, below is a list of the terms used throughout this book with a brief definition and sometimes some editorial commentary. And, to make it easier, I will tell you whether the term is good or bad. Mostly that's an easy call, and don't worry, there are more good terms than bad terms on this list.

Acute Mountain Sickness. Acute Mountain Sickness, or AMS, is a mild sickness brought about by high elevation. Acute Mountain Sickness is <u>bad</u>. It's a headache without even the joy of drinking copious quantities of alcohol the night before.

Adiabatic Cooling. Adiabatic cooling is the cooling of a body of air as it rises in the atmosphere caused by its expansion. Adiabatic cooling is <u>good</u>. It means the mountains are colder than the plains and therefore snowier. I suppose a cross-country skier might disagree and say it is bad as they want snow on the plains. But trust me, adiabatic cooling is good.

Adiabatic Heating. Adiabatic heating is the heating of a body of air as it descends in the atmosphere caused by its compression. Adiabatic heating is <u>bad</u>. It prevents snow from falling in the precipitation shadow of mountains. I guess it's only good for people who like the turbochargers in their cars or their pressure cookers.

The American Model. The American Model, also known as the GFS (i.e., Global Forecast System) Model, is one of the primary global numerical weather prediction computer models in the world. It is run by the National Weather Service. The American Model is <u>good</u>, as it helps us predict snow.

Anticyclone. An anticyclone is another word for high pressure. High pressure is <u>bad</u>.

Avalanche. An avalanche is a mass of snow moving down the mountain. Avalanches are <u>bad</u>. I've lost too many friends and acquaintances to them.

Barometer. A barometer is an instrument that measures atmospheric pressure. A barometer is <u>good</u>, especially when it is going down. Barometers tell you what is happening with the weather, and a dropping pressure indicates snow is likely to be on its way.

Bergschrund. A bergschrund is a crevasse at the top of a glacier, where the glacier pulls away from the mountain and snow above it. It is often the biggest crevasse, and sometimes the only visible crevasse, on the glacier. A bergschrund is <u>bad</u>, especially if you fall into it.

Block. Blocks are large-scale patterns in atmospheric pressure that block other weather. A block is <u>good</u> if it refers to a trough blocking a ridge, but it is <u>bad</u> if it refers to a ridge blocking a trough. It is more commonly used in the bad sense.

Blocking Ridge. A blocking ridge is a ridge where the air mass is blocking low pressure systems / troughs. A blocking ridge is <u>bad</u>. It keeps snow away from Colorado. Boo!

Bomb Cyclone. A bomb cyclone is a low pressure (i.e., a cyclone) system where the pressure decreases at least 24 millibars (hPA) in 24 hours. A bomb cyclone is <u>good</u>, just like any low pressure system, as it creates snow. Frankly, this is not a term used frequently by forecasters, but boy does the media love this scary sounding name.

The Butterfly Effect. The butterfly effect is the principle in chaos theory that even the most seemingly minor changes in the inputs into a system will drastically affect the eventual outputs of a system, usually in unpredictable ways. It is also referred to by the far less memorable name of: the sensitive dependence on initial conditions. The butterfly effect is <u>bad</u> as it makes predicting snow more difficult. Unless of course you are skiing on the day there is a huge unpredicted snowstorm, in which case the butterfly effect is good.

The Canadian Model. The Canadian Model, also known as the GDPS (i.e., Global Deterministic Prediction Systems) Model, is one of the global numerical weather prediction computer models, eh. The Canadian Model is <u>good</u>, eh, as it helps us predict snow, eh.

Celsius – A silly temperature scale that puts the cold winter temperature in Golden as -18 degrees and the hot summer temperature in Golden as 38 degrees. It is apparently based off the freezing point of impure water as 0 degrees if we ignore evaporative cooling; and the boiling point of water as 100 degrees if we all lived at sea level, which we most certainly do not in Colorado. At the risk of being controversial, while the Celsius scale may work well for chefs who live in Miami, the Celsius scale is <u>bad</u> as it is not nearly as useful or logical for real world conditions as Fahrenheit.

Chinook. Chinook winds, also known as Foehn winds, are warm dry winds that descend the lee side (i.e., the eastern side) of the Rocky Mountains. Chinook winds are <u>bad</u>. They are often called "snow eaters" as they can strip a lee aspect of snow rather quickly.

Cirque. A cirque is the top of a valley, just below a ridge, formed by glacial erosion. They tend to have a steep cup shape to them. Cirques are <u>good</u>, as most of the glaciers in Colorado are found in cirques.

Climate. Climate is the average weather at a location. Climate is <u>good</u> as Colorado has an awesome climate. Unfortunately, on average the worldwide climate is warming, which is bad as that will be bad for skiing. If the world-wide climate was cooling instead, that would be good.

Closed low. A closed low is a low pressure system that typically is partially cut off from the main westerly flow of winds, but is not completely removed from the influence of the westerly winds. A closed low is good as it typically produces lots of snow, but it is not quite as good as a cutoff low.

Cold Front. A cold front is where an airmass of colder air is advancing and replacing an airmass of warmer air. A cold front is good, as it usually brings in snow – usually for a short but intense period of time.

Condensation Nuclei. Condensation nuclei are tiny particles on which water vapor condenses. Condensation Nuclei are good. Without them, microscopic water droplets that are the building blocks of snow crystals would not form in clouds.

Continental Divide. The continental divide is the line running (very roughly) from north to south through the Rocky Mountains, which divides the watersheds of the Atlantic and Pacific Ocean. The continental divide is good, as it tends to be really high in Colorado, which means more orographic lift, which means more snow.

Continental Snow. Continental snow is light density snow found in mountain regions far from any ocean. Colorado has continental snow. Continental snow is good. We all like light and fluffy powder.

Convection. Convection is the vertical transport of heat and moisture in the atmosphere, especially by updrafts. Thunderstorms are the most well-known type of convection. Convection is bad. It rarely brings snow, but often brings lightning.

Coriolis Effect. The Coriolis effect is the pattern of deflection objects in the atmosphere take as observed from the earth due to the fact that the earth spins around its own axis. The Coriolis effect is <u>good</u> because otherwise the earth would not rotate, and it would always be way too dark on one side or way too sunny on the other.

Corn Snow. Corn snow is a snow condition caused by the large rounded crystals of the snow near the surface. It is formed by repeated melting and freezing of the snow surface, usually during springtime. Corn snow is <u>good</u>. It's fun to ski.

Cornice. A cornice is an overhanging or vertical mass of snow created by eddies in the wind. A cornice is <u>bad</u> as it's not good when it collapses. But smaller ones are fun to catch air on, so they're not all bad.

Crevasse. A crevasse is a deep fissure or hole in the snow. Crevasses are caused by gravity overwhelming the snow's cohesion with itself. They are few and far between in Colorado. A crevasse is <u>bad</u>, especially if you fall into it.

Cutoff Low. A cutoff low is a low pressure system that has been completely cut off from the main flow of winds from the west. Cutoff lows can remain nearly stationary for days meandering about. A closed low is a similar pattern, but a closed low is not completely removed from the influence of the winds from the west. A cutoff low is <u>good</u>. It can produce tremendously large storms.

Cyclone. A cyclone is another word for low pressure. Low pressure is <u>good</u>.

Depression. For our purposes, a depression is another word for a low pressure area. A depression is <u>good</u>. It means snow.

Dillon Donut. The Dillon Donut is the lower elevation area around Dillon where there is less snow than one would expect due to the high peaks nearly encircling Dillon. The Dillon Donut is <u>good</u>, as it provides a respite for drivers on snowy roads before they climb out of the donut to ski the higher and snowier places.

Diurnal Recrystallization. Diurnal recrystallization is faceted snow created by large temperature gradients from both the day air (warm) and the night air (cold). Diurnal recrystallization is <u>good</u> as it creates arguably the best recycled powder. It's just bad from an avalanche perspective once it gets buried under more layers of snow.

Eddy. An eddy is a swirling current of air going the opposite direction from the main current of air. Eddies are <u>good</u> as they create pillows, and on a larger scale they help create other weather phenomenon that leads to more snow.

Ensemble Forecast. An ensemble forecast is a collection of numerical model forecasts results showing different potential weather outcomes. An ensemble forecast is <u>good</u>, as it helps us predict snow.

The European Model. The European Model (or technically the Integrated Forecast System of the European Centre for Medium-Range Weather Forecasts, wow that's a mouthful) is one of the primary global numerical weather prediction computer models in the world. The European Model is <u>good</u>, as it helps us predict snow.

Evaporative Cooling. Evaporative cooling is the cooling of an object by the evaporation of liquid on the surface of the body. Evaporative cooling is <u>good</u> as it allows ski resorts to make snow at higher temperatures. Of course, any term with the word cooling in it is generally a good term.

Facets. Facets are angular large grained snow crystals created by large temperature gradients in the snowpack. Facets are <u>bad</u> as they create a sliding layer for avalanches (unless they constitute the top layer of the snow, and you're skiing them. If so, we call them recycled powder, and recycled powder is good).

Fahrenheit – A more logical temperature scale than Celsius, which puts the cold winter-time temperature in Golden as 0 degrees and the hot summer temperature in Golden as 100 degrees. It is derogatorily known as freedom units. Fahrenheit is <u>good</u>, as it measures temperature and makes more sense than Celsius.

Fetches. Fetches is what dogs love to do. Just kidding. Fetches are the areas from which wind transports snow, and often after a wind cycle are largely devoid of snow. Fetches are <u>good</u> (and I know this is a glass half full view) because if they didn't provide a source of snow, the leeward sides of mountains would have less snow.

Forecast Fairyland. Forecast fairyland is when there is too much time between when the forecast is made and when the weather is supposed to occur. In forecast fairyland the forecast has basically no predictive value. In meteorology speak, the forecast is not "skillful" because the forecast is not more likely to occur than the historical baseline weather. Forecast fairyland is <u>bad</u>, as we wish it didn't exist and forecasts were better.

Freezing Nuclei. Freezing nuclei are tiny particles on which ice crystals form. Freezing nuclei are <u>good</u>. Without them, snow crystals could not form, and it would never snow unless the cloud temperature was below minus forty degrees, which is virtually too cold a temperature to snow anyhow.

Front Range. The Front Range of Colorado is the eastern most mountains and the urban corridor beneath it. Think of it as running from Fort Collins in the north – through Boulder, Denver, and Colorado Springs – to Pueblo in the south. The Front Range is <u>good</u> as that is where I live. Of course, when there are traffic jams on I-70 westbound headed towards Colorado ski areas, most people do not think the Front Range is good.

Fronts. A front is the boundary zone between two air masses usually of different temperatures. Typically, one of the air masses is advancing into the other air mass. Fronts are <u>good</u>. They bring snow.

Frostbite. Frostbite is damage to human body tissue, usually near or at the skin, from cells freezing and dying. Frostbite is <u>bad</u>.

Gapers. Gapers are the losers who gape at the real skiers. Gapers often ski where they shouldn't, hike in the skin track, fail to carry avalanche gear, drive I-70 in two-wheel drive vehicles, and do not follow avalanche protocols. Usually, they've never taken an avalanche class. Gapers are <u>bad</u>. Don't be a gaper. And don't hike in the skin track gaper assholes!

Glacier. A glacier is a permanent snowfield (that is, a snowfield that doesn't disappear in the late summer / early fall), that people call a glacier with either the official name or a local name. Anyhow, that's my working definition of a glacier, and I'm sure this definition will generate several angry emails with a myriad of other differing definitions. There are a few handfuls of glaciers in Colorado – often called Cirque Glaciers. A glacier is <u>good</u> because it provides snow to ski on in the late summer and early fall when there is almost no snow anywhere else.

GNAR. GNAR is Gaffney's Numerical Assessment of Radness. Watch the Unofficial Networks Movie. GNAR points are <u>good</u>.

Gravity Waves. Gravity waves are the complicated sounding word for the vertical movement of an air parcel in a wave pattern. In other words, the wave pattern is bouncing as it heads downwind. Gravity waves are <u>good</u> if the air parcel's vertical movement upwards is enough to produce more snow. But, they rarely do that. That said, I suppose the rare snow shower is better than no snow at all.

Great Basin. The Great Basin is the area constituting most of Nevada, some of Utah, and a bit of California and Oregon, where none of the water flows into an ocean. Basically, think of everything from Squaw Valley to Snowbird as the Great Basin. The Great Basin is <u>good</u>. Besides having its own amazing skiing, when Colorado forecasters say the storm is over the Great Basin, that usually means we'll be seeing it next.

High Altitude Pulmonary Edema (HAPE). HAPE is a condition where fluid accumulates in the lungs due to high altitude. HAPE is <u>bad</u>.

High Pressure System. A high pressure system is a region of high air pressure, where the vertical motion of the air is down towards the ground. High pressure is <u>bad</u>, unless you want to work on your tan, or it's situated in northeast Colorado with decent moisture. But, as high pressure helps creates wind, and wind (when rising) creates snow, a high pressure system in the right spots can be good.

Hypothermia. Hypothermia is when the body temperature falls to an abnormal temperature, usually below 95 degrees Fahrenheit (35 degrees Celsius). Hypothermia is <u>bad</u>.

Ice Lens. An ice lens is a very hard layer in a snowpack, usually formed by melting and then freezing of the snow. Think of a suncrust that has been buried by more recent snow. An ice lens is <u>bad</u> because when buried it creates a sliding surface for avalanches. Plus, even on the surface they're not fun to ski.

Intermountain Snow. Intermountain snow is the type of snow found in areas not as close to the ocean as the maritime climate, but not as far inland as the continental climate. This is medium-density snow. Intermountain snow is <u>good</u>. While it may not be truly light and fluffy, it at least builds a good snow base.

Jet Contrail. A jet contrail is the cirrus cloud formed by water vapor and other exhaust being thrust out the back of a jet engine in the upper troposphere. Jet contrails are <u>good</u>, as they are one of the best visual clues on the weather in the upper atmosphere. That said, they are hardly as reliable as the sophisticated weather models in predicting future weather.

Jet Streak. The jet streak is the area within the jet stream with the maximum wind speeds. The jet streak is <u>good</u>, as it produces lift on the right side (usually south) of its entrance and left side (usually north) of its exit, which both produce snow.

Jet Stream. The jet stream is a relatively narrow band of intense wind in the upper atmosphere that runs from west to east around the globe. The jet stream is <u>good</u>, especially when it brings long wave troughs over Colorado as that means snow.

Laminar Flow. Laminar flow is smooth nonturbulent flow of air (or any other fluid). Laminar flow is <u>good</u> because wind is good. See wind.

Lapse Rate. Lapse rates compare the change of temperature with the gain in elevation. A steep positive lapse rate implies a rapid decrease in temperature with height, while a shallow positive lapse rate implies a gradual decrease in temperature with height. A negative lapse rate shows a temperature inversion. I could perhaps better describe this using an equation, but as I promised, there are no equations in this book. The lapse rate is <u>good</u>, as it measures adiabatic cooling. And without adiabatic cooling, there would basically be no snow in Colorado.

Leeward. Leeward is the downwind side of a ridge or mountain. Leeward is <u>good</u>, as the wind blows snow onto the leeward slopes. (I'm definitely the glass half full type, as I also say the opposite of leeward, windward, is good as well. A bit of Professor Pangloss, I must admit.)

Lightning. Gosh, do I really have to define lightning? Lightning is a visible electrical discharge produced by a thunderstorm accompanied by a loud boom. The loud boom is also known as thunder. Lightning is <u>bad</u>. Not only can it be deadly, but to add insult to injury, it also shuts down chairlifts.

Long wave. A long wave, also known as a Rossby wave, is the pattern of upper-altitude winds between the polar and temperate air masses that, surprise, move in a wave pattern. Long waves are <u>good</u> if they bring cold and snow.

Low Pressure System. A low pressure system is a region of low air pressure, where the vertical motion of the air is upwards and away from the ground. A low pressure system is <u>good</u>. It means snow.

Maritime Snow. Maritime snow is the type of snow found close to the ocean, which is typically high-density snow. Maritime snow is <u>good</u> because all snow is good. It is not as good, however, as continental snow as it is denser.

Mesoscale. The mesoscale is the weather scale smaller than the synoptic scale but larger than the mountain (or subgrid) scale. It's often considered to be on the size of roughly 10 to 100 miles. The mesoscale is <u>good</u>, as it gives us a good idea of the weather in the shorter time horizon.

Moats. Moats are crevasse like holes in snow, usually found in the late-spring through late-fall, caused by warmth of rocks and/or running water. Moats are <u>bad</u>. You don't want to fall into one.

Mountains. Mountains are landforms that rise above the surrounding area. Mountains are <u>good</u>. They create snow (through Orographic Lifting) and are fun to ski on.

The NAM Model. The NAM (North American Meso) is a regional numerical weather prediction computer model. The NAM Model is <u>good</u>, as it helps us predict snow.

Orographic Lifting. Orographic lifting is proof that god loves us and wants us to be happy (sorry Ben Franklin to have shamelessly stolen and restated your quote about wine). Orographic lifting is when an air mass is forced to rise to get over a hill or mountain and therefore cools. And cooling air produces snow. Orographic lifting is <u>good</u>. It produces a majority of the snow in the Colorado mountains.

Pillow. A pillow is an area of snow deposited just downwind of a ridge. Pillows are <u>good</u> because they're fun to ski, unless they serve as a spot where an avalanche starts.

Pineapple Express. The pineapple express is the strong and persistent flow of moisture from the Pacific Ocean near Hawaii to the North American continent. The pineapple express is <u>good</u>, especially if you like to ski at Wolf Creek.

Point Forecast. A point forecast is a model generated forecast (i.e., a numerical weather prediction computer model generated forecast) for a specific point on the map. Point forecasts are <u>good</u>, as they help predict powder. But, as much as I love them, be wary of looking only at them in forecasting as you can miss the predicted forest for the predicted trees.

Powder. Powder is the reason why you are reading this book. Perhaps it is the reason why life is worth living. It is the result of large snow crystals on the top layer of the snowpack. Powder is <u>good</u>.

Precipitation Shadow. A precipitation shadow is an area of reduced precipitation on the lee (downwind) side of a tall mountain or ridge. It appears on small scales and big scales. On a big scale, the Rocky Mountains of Colorado cause a precipitation shadow that extends from the foothills to a third of the way across Kansas. A precipitation shadow is <u>bad</u> if you are in it and want snow where you are.

The RDPS Model. The RDPS (Regional Deterministic Prediction Systems) is a regional numerical weather prediction computer model from Canada, eh. The RDPS Model is <u>good</u>, eh, as it helps us predict snow, eh.

Recycled Powder. Recycled Powder is snow that has gone through the faceting process (see facets) that is still on the top layer (that is, the surface layer). Recycled powder is <u>good</u>. All powder is good. (At least it's good until it gets buried and forms a weak layer.)

Relative Humidity. Relative humidity is the percentage of water vapor in an air parcel compared to the maximum amount the air parcel can hold. Relative humidity is <u>good</u>, especially when the number is high and it is cold. In weather models, a forecasted relative humidity between 70% and 90% is usually indicative of clouds, and relative humidity above 90% is usually indicative of precipitation.

Reynolds Number. The Reynolds number determines whether air flow will be laminar or turbulent, which in turn impacts how snow is deposited by wind. I'd explain this more, but I promised no equations in this book, so you'll just have to google it if you want to know more. The Reynolds number is <u>good</u>, as it helps us understand the wind deposit of snow.

Ridge (meteorology). A ridge is an elongated area of relatively high pressure. It is the opposite of a trough. A ridge (i.e., the meteorological term) is <u>bad</u>. It means no snow. But as glass half-full types, remember it does mean more pleasant weather to be skiing in.

Ridge (topography). A ridge is a long narrow hilltop or mountain. A ridge (i.e., the topographical term) is <u>good</u>, as anything related to mountains is good.

Rounds. Rounds are ice grains formed by snow on the ground when there is little or no crystal growth. Rounds, if on top of facets, are <u>bad</u>. Heck, even if they're not on top of facets, they still aren't powder. So, let's keep them in the bad column.

Saltation. Saltation is the act of putting more salt on your French Fries at the base lodge. Just kidding. Saltation is a mode of transport for snow caused by the wind in which the snow particles bounce along the snow surface, not getting higher than about four inches above the surface. Saltation is <u>good</u>, it is the primary way snow is transferred by the wind.

Skunked. Getting skunked is when you expect to ski powder based upon weather forecasts that don't pan out, so you're either skiing no fresh powder or just dust on crust. Being skunked is <u>bad</u>.

SNOTEL Site. A Snotel Site (SNOTEL stands for SNOw TELemetry) is an automated system of snowpack and related climate sensors that provide data on the amount of new snowfall and other pertinent information to skiers. As Snotel sites report snow, they are <u>good</u>.

Snow. Okay, do I really need to define snow? Well, if I must define it, I'll just steal the National Weather Service's definition word-for-word. Snow is "precipitation in the form of ice crystals, mainly of intricately branched, hexagonal form and often agglomerated into snowflakes, formed directly from the freezing [deposition] of the water vapor in the air." There, are you happy I defined it? Snow is good. Duh.

Snow Crystal. A snow crystal is a single six-sided crystal of ice. Snow crystal form snowflakes. Snowflakes create snow. So, snow crystals are good.

Snowflake. A snowflake is a group of snow crystals falling as a unit. Snowflakes create snow, so snowflakes are good.

Snow Fence. A snow fence is a fence that helps snow accumulate immediately downwind of the fence. Snow fences are good as they keep powder on ski runs as opposed to letting the snow blow into the next county.

Snow Immersion Suffocation. Snow Immersion Suffocation is an accident in which a skier falls, usually headfirst, into a tree well or deep loose snow resulting in immobilization and suffocation. Snow Immersion Suffocation is bad.

Snowpack. Snowpack is the total snow on the ground, which includes both the new and old snow. The snowpack is good, especially when it is deep.

Snow Stake. A snow stake is a square semi-permanent stake, marked in inch increments to measure snow depth. A snow stake is good as it measures the depth of the snow.

Snow Water Equivalent. Snow water equivalent is the water content obtained from melting the accumulated snow. It is abbreviated as SWE, pronounced like "sweet" without the "t" sound at the end. Snow water equivalent is good, as it is a good way to measure how much snow there is.

Spillover Effect. The spillover effect is the meteorological phenomenon that an airmass does not just produce snow on the upwind (i.e., windward) side of the mountain, but also produces snow on the initial portion of the downwind (i.e., leeward) side of the mountain. The spillover effect is good. Without it, there wouldn't be nearly as much snow in Breckenridge, Loveland, Monarch, and Wolf Creek, among other places.

Stellar Dendrites. Stellar dendrites are relatively large sized snow crystals with long branches. Stellar dendrites are good. They are the best type of snow crystal for powder skiing.

Storm. A storm is a disturbed state in the atmosphere usually causing precipitation. Storms are good, as long as they produce snow.

Stratosphere. The stratosphere is the part of the earth's atmosphere above the troposphere. Weather usually does not occur in the stratosphere – it's too stratospheric! The stratosphere is good, because we like our atmosphere, and the stratosphere is part of it.

Subgrid. Forecast models calculate weather based upon grids. When features – whether large like peaks, ridges, bowls, etc. or small like trees, snow fences, etc. – are too small to be picked up in a grid cell, they are called subgrid. Subgrid is bad, as it's one of the reasons why computer forecasting models cannot accurately predict snowfall where you'll be skiing.

Sublimation. Sublimation is the transition of ice directly to water vapor without passing through the intermediate liquid water phase. When only looking at Colorado, sublimation is bad, as it means we lose snow to the atmosphere in windy conditions.

Supercooled. Supercooled water is liquid water (as opposed to frozen water) that is colder than 32 degrees Fahrenheit (0 degrees Celsius). Supercooled water is good because it helps form snow.

Surface Hoar. Get your mind out of the gutter. Surface hoar is frost that forms on the surface of the snow. It is frozen dew. Surface hoar is <u>bad</u>. Once it's buried under more snow, it's the most likely sliding layer that causes avalanche fatalities in Colorado.

Synoptic Scale. The synoptic scale is the weather scale larger than the mesoscale but smaller than the hemispheric scale. It's often considered to be on the size of roughly 100 to 1000 miles. The synoptic scale is <u>good</u>, as it gives us a good idea of weather over the medium horizon.

Tree. Come on. You know what a tree is. A tree is <u>good</u>. It keeps snow from blowing away. Just don't get too close to one when skiing.

Treeline. The treeline is the top elevation at which trees can grow. Above treeline there are basically no trees. Treeline is <u>good</u>, as it gives us more options to find powder – because sometimes its better below treeline and sometimes its better above treeline.

Troposphere. The troposphere is the bottom layer in the atmosphere and the one in which virtually all weather occurs. Its height varies by latitude and season, but to give you a general sense, think seven and a half miles up from sea level, or 40,000 feet, is the height of the top of the troposphere. The troposphere is <u>good</u> as it is the part of the atmosphere in which weather happens, and weather is good.

Trough. A trough is an elongated area of relatively low pressure. It is the opposite of a ridge. A trough is <u>good</u>. It means snow.

Turbulence. Turbulence is irregular motions in the atmosphere usually accompanied by gusts and lulls in the wind. Turbulence often causes eddies that help deposit snow. Turbulence is <u>good</u> because wind is good. See wind.

Turbulent Suspension. Turbulent suspension is a mode of snow transport by wind when wind speeds exceed roughly 35 miles per hour, in which turbulent eddies lift the snow well above the surface. Turbulent suspension is bad, I suppose. While wind transport of snow is good, turbulent suspension causes snow to be lost to sublimation which is bad, not to mention the fact that it makes for ugly driving conditions. So, I suppose overall if I have to choose either good or bad, its more bad than good.

The UKMET Model. The UKMET Model is one of the primary global numerical weather prediction computer models in the world. It is run by the United Kingdom METeorological Agency, which is how it gets its name. The UKMET Model is good, as it helps us predict snow.

Upslope storm. An upslope storm, as referred to in Colorado, is a storm where the winds come from the east causing more snow to the east of the continental divide. An upslope storm is good, especially if you like to ski to the east of the continental divide.

Vorticity. Vorticity is the measure of the spin of a system. If it is positive, that means that the air parcel will be lifting, which is good because that produces snow. See low pressure system.

Warm Front. A warm front is where an air mass of warmer air is advancing and replacing an air mass of colder air. A warm front is good as it may create snow.

Water Content. Water content is the amount of water obtained from melting a certain amount of snow, usually expressed as the ratio of the volume of snow to melted water. As a rough rule of thumb, under 8% water content is light snow, 8 to 12% is average snow, and over 12% is heavy snow. Water content is good, as without it there would not be snow. And water content is especially good when it's at low percentages.

Water Vapor. Water vapor is water in the gas phase, as opposed to liquid or solid phase. Water vapor is good. When it rises (i.e., cools) it is the essential ingredient in creating snow.

Weather. Weather is the state of the atmosphere at a given time and location. Weather is <u>good</u>, especially when the current state of the atmosphere is snowing like mad.

Wind. Wind is the motion of air past a given point. It is caused by trees sneezing. Okay, that's not true, I just wanted to see if anyone is still paying attention. There are numerous causes of wind, but the primary one is the fact that air moves from areas of high pressure to areas of low pressure. Wind is <u>good</u>. Without wind, water vapor from the Pacific Ocean would never make it to Colorado, so we'd have no snow. That would suck. So, the next time you complain about how windy it is, don't forget it's the only reason we can ski powder.

Windward. Windward is the upwind side of a ridge or mountain. Windward is <u>good</u>, as the wind blows the cloud up and over the windward side, so it snows. (I lead a good life, as I also say the opposite of windward, leeward, is good as well.)

The WRF Model. The WRF (Weather Research and Forecasting Model) is a regional numerical weather prediction computer model. The WRF Model is <u>good</u>, as it helps us predict snow.

Z. Z is the sound you're making if you're still trying to read this glossary. It's also the abbreviation for Zulu time, which is the same thing as Coordinated Universal Time or UTC, which is basically the same thing as Greenwich Mean Time. Z is <u>good</u> as it keeps weather maps throughout a myriad of time zones all showing the same time, though it's confusing to always think in London time.

About the Author

Jordan Lipp started skiing at Swain Ski Area in New York State at age 2 and started ski patrolling at Swain at age 16. He moved to Colorado as soon as he could, when he was 18 (and he moved to Colorado supposedly for college). He patrolled at Eldora for a year, and then he patrolled for three years at the old Berthoud Pass Ski Area where he also became an avalanche safety instructor and an outdoor emergency care instructor. After three adventurous years patrolling at one of Colorado's snowiest, steepest, and most avalanche-prone spots, in perhaps not the smartest decision when it comes to skiing, he moved to Michigan to go to law school. Nevertheless, he continued patrolling during school breaks at Berthoud Pass, and during the school year he patrolled at one of the southern Michigan's landfill ski areas. While in Michigan, the Berthoud Pass Ski Area shut down. So, on his return to Colorado, Jordan found that his old stomping ground had lost its chairlifts but was now a backcountry paradise.

Based upon his patrolling time and subsequent backcountry skiing at Berthoud Pass, in 2005 he authored the book: *Backcountry Skiing Berthoud Pass: A Guidebook to Skiing and Snowboarding Berthoud Pass, Colorado.* And in spite of the Berthoud Pass Ski Area shutting down, Jordan kept volunteer ski patrolling.

He joined the Bryan Mountain Nordic Ski Patrol – patrolling at both the cross-country area Devil's Thumb Ranch and in the backcountry of Colorado's front range. He continues to teach avalanche classes through the ski patrol, and especially loves teaching weather and snow science. And, he puts together the weather forecasts for the Bryan Mountain Nordic Ski Patrol's backcountry portion of its patrol.

As Jordan loves to ski and snowboard, he has skied all 33 operating ski areas in Colorado. And, he has skied at over one hundred different ski areas all over the world. He has skied in many exotic locations, from the Greater Baekdu Mountains of Korea to the Atlas Mountains of Morocco, and from the Talkeetna Mountains of Alaska to the Snowy Mountains of Australia. He makes sure to ski at least one day every month of the year in Colorado – with his current streak going for a little over a decade now. And, if counting up accomplishments, he's broken eleven bones skiing, but is that really an accomplishment?

Jordan hates writing in the third person, and he doesn't understand why every "about the author" in every book is written in the third person.

When not skiing, snowboarding, or geeking out on weather, Jordan lives with his wife and two children in Golden, Colorado. He works as an attorney in Denver, Colorado, where he is fortunate enough to have a portion of his law practice involving the representation of ski areas and other outdoor recreation companies in litigation.

And like father, like kids – at age seven Jordan's daughter completed skiing all of Colorado's 33 operating ski areas, and at age five Jordan's son had skied at least one day every month of the year in Colorado. Jordan and his family lead a rough life, but someone has to do it.